The Young Specialist Looks At

Land and Freshwater Molluscs

The Young Specialist Looks At
Land and Freshwater
Molluscs

HORST JANUS

Translated, edited and adapted

Illustrated by Walter Söllner and Cynthia O'Brien

BURKE  LONDON

First published in the English language, April 1965
© BURKE PUBLISHING COMPANY LIMITED, 1965

Translated and adapted from *Unsere Schnecken und Muscheln*
© Franckh'sche Verlagshandlung, W. Keller & Co., Stuttgart, 1958

ACKNOWLEDGEMENT

The publishers are grateful to Messrs. Paul Popper for permission to reproduce the Margiocco photograph of the Common Snail, *Helix aspersa*, which appears on the cover of this book.

BURKE PUBLISHING COMPANY LTD.
14 JOHN STREET ★ LONDON, W.C.1

Set in Monophoto Times New Roman
Made and printed by offset in Great Britain by
William Clowes and Sons, Limited, London and Beccles

Contents

List of Plates

Symbols and Abbreviations

H = height
B = breadth
L = length
W = number of whorls
TS = transverse section

Note: Height and breadth and length are given in millimetres as is normal scientific practice. (A comparison with inches is given on this page.) The scale lines against each drawing show the actual length of the animal or the actual height or breadth of the shell; divided scale lines indicate the normal range of variation of such dimensions.

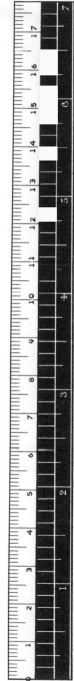

Scale showing inches and centimetres

7

Foreword

This book covers all the 178 species of Snails, Slugs and Freshwater Mussels which are either native to the British Isles or have succeeded in establishing themselves in the wild state in these islands after introduction or reintroduction from elsewhere.

The text and illustrations present an elementary account of our non-marine molluscs which should serve as a satisfactory introduction to the works recommended for further reading in the Bibliography on page 168. A conservative classification has been adopted to facilitate correlation with those employed in more advanced books. Apart from a few well-justified exceptions, the names of species are those used in the Conchological Society's list but the translator has been rather more free with his recognition of subgenera—partly to indicate the natural groupings within the larger genera and partly to help reconcile the nomenclature with that to be found in earlier literature. A number of the more frequent synonyms have, however, been included in the Index.

The translator has considerably augmented his translation of Dr. Horst Janus' original book by expanding the text and introducing a good deal of further material. Some discussion of marine molluscs has been added in order to present the land and freshwater species in their true perspective, the general anatomical and classificatory sections have been revised and enlarged and text and illustrations covering 89 additional species have been inserted at appropriate points among the original species descriptions. The translator wishes to acknowledge his debt to the publications by Barnes, Comfort, Ellis, Fretter & Graham, Jeffreys, Kevan, Kuiper, Moquin-Tandon, Quick, Step, Wenzt and Winckworth to which he referred in preparing this additional information and to thank the kind friends who lent him much of this literature.

An introductory account of each family has been added to the systematic section of the book and a number of original keys to identification have also been provided. The publishers wish, however, to express their thanks to the Council of the Linnean Society for permission to reproduce the key to *Pisidium* which first appeared in A. E. Ellis' *British Freshwater Bivalve Molluscs* (*Synopses of the British Fauna* No. 13, 1962).

9

Part One

Snails, Slugs and Freshwater Mussels

What They Are, and How to Recognise Them

Systematic zoologists—the people who concern themselves with the scientific classification of animals—put snails, slugs and freshwater mussels together in one of the major divisions of the Animal Kingdom: the Phylum Mollusca (= "soft-bodied ones", from the Latin *molluscus*, soft). Within this phylum they form parts of two sub-divisions or Classes. Now the Molluscs are a very successful, diverse and widespread group, including some 112,000 different species. They are also a very ancient group; they have "been around" for over 400 million years—longer than the most primitive vertebrates and over ten thousand *times* longer than our own species. They owe this success to the fact that their structural ground-plan was capable of adaptation to a wide variety of conditions and modes of life. Its only real limitation was a dependence upon at least intermittently damp conditions, necessitated by only moderately satisfactory adaptations to cope with the problems of air-breathing and desiccation of the soft body. However, molluscs of one kind or another are found from the tops of tall trees down to the great deeps of the oceans, and if they have had little success in conquering the air they have at least produced Flying Squids (*Ommastrephes*) to parallel the various fish-groups which have attained to brief gliding flight.

Large groups of molluscs are still confined to the sea which gave rise to them in the first place, way back in the remote Cambrian period: land and freshwater species may be regarded as the descendants of successful colonists. It will be useful, therefore, to take a quick look at the general classification of the whole phylum so as to see the land and freshwater molluscs in their proper context; groups dealt with in this book are shown in heavy type.

11

Phylum Mollusca

Class I. Amphineura ("paired-nerved ones": Greek *amphi*, double, on both sides, and *neuron*, a nerve).
Primitive molluscs which have a centralised nervous system with two lateral strands. Include the chitons, which have a segmented shell of eight plates, looking rather like a wood-louse; the worm-like *Neomenia* and its relatives; the deep-sea "living fossil" *Neopilina*. All marine.

Class 2. Gastropoda ("belly-footed ones": Greek *gaster*, belly, stomach and *pous*, *podos*, foot).
Molluscs whose ventral surface forms a creeping sole or foot; which have a head with sensory tentacles; whose body is usually twisted at some stage, and is generally protected by a shell composed all of one piece ("univalves"). Include many sea-snails (whelks, limpets, etc.); sea-slugs and sea-hares; the drifting marine pteropods or sea-butterflies; **freshwater snails; land snails; land slugs**.

Class 3. Scaphopoda ("shovel-footed ones": Greek *skapis*, a shovel and *pous*, *podos*, a foot).
Burrowing molluscs with a reduced foot, used for digging; head with peculiar grasping organs but no sense-organs; shell in one piece, shaped like a hollow elephant's tusk, open at both ends; no gills or heart. Include only tusk-shells. All marine.

Class 4. Lamellibranchiata ("leaf-gilled ones": Latin *lamella*, a thin plate or leaf and Greek plural *branchia*, the gills of fishes).
Molluscs with a foot used for ploughing or burrowing; a greatly reduced head; a compressed body contained within a shell composed of two halves or valves ("bivalves"); complicated leaf-like or curtain-like gills used for filter-feeding. Entirely aquatic, except that some mussels, etc. can withstand exposure at low tide. Include many marine bivalves (mussels, scallops, clams, oysters, cockles, piddocks, ship-worms, etc.) and **freshwater mussels**.

Class 5. Cephalopoda ("head-footed ones": Greek *kephale*, a head and *pous*, *podos*, a foot).
Molluscs with a well-developed head surrounded by a crown of sucker-bearing tentacles representing a much-divided foot; mantle-opening produced to form a siphon, used for backward jet-propulsion; a chambered shell; a greatly-centralised brain and elaborate eyes. Include octopuses, squids, cuttlefishes, pearly nautilus, paper nautilus and extinct ammonites. All marine.

Readers of this book will already have some knowledge of natural history and will recognise enough familiar creatures to make some sense of the above catalogue. We will clarify the rest as we go along.

12

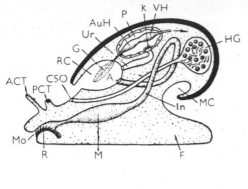

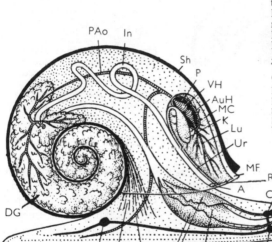

Figure 1. Schematic diagram of the structure of a generalised snail. (For key to lettering see legend to Figure 2, below.) (After Kühn.)

Figure 2. Internal anatomy of a snail. A Anus, AAo Anterior Aorta, ACT Anterior Cephalic Tentacles, AuH Auricle of Heart, Cr Crop, CG Cerebral Ganglia, CM Columella Muscle, CSO Common Sexual Opening, DG Digestive Gland ("Liver"), F Foot, G Gill, HG Hermaphrodite Gland (Ovotestis), In Intestine, J Jaw, K Kidney, Lu Lung (capillary network), MC Mantle-cavity, MF Mantle-fold, Mo Mouth, P Pericardium, PAo Posterior Aorta, PCT Posterior Cephalic Tentacles (eye-stalks), PG Pedal Ganglia, R Radula, RA Respiratory Aperture, RC Respiratory Chamber (part of mantle-cavity), Sh Shell, SG Salivary Glands, Ur Ureter, VH Ventricle of Heart, VG Visceral Ganglion.

Snails, slugs and freshwater mussels have many characters in common which are, of course, those which pertain to molluscs in general. Whatever the eventual complications of their development, all of them are animals with a fundamentally bilateral symmetry (i.e. they are divisible into two mirror-image halves on either side of a median plane) and a soft, compact body whose basic structural plan comprises four divisions: head, visceral mass, mantle and foot. The last three can be considered together and called the trunk.

Molluscs do not have an internal skeleton; instead, most of them secrete an external or exo-skeleton, the shell or "house". We shall consider this in some detail and above all learn about its formation and structure because, in snails and mussels especially, the shell is,

13

so to speak, the animal's visiting-card which provides many convenient clues to the recognition of individual species; in the
majority of cases it is possible to make a positive identification on
shell-characters alone.

The molluscan shell is a lifeless part of the body, comparable in
this respect with the horny appendages of vertebrate animals (hair,
feathers, hooves, nails and claws). It is secreted by the edge of the
mantle—a glandular fold of skin arising from the back and en-
veloping the visceral mass within a visceral sac. The basic material
of the shell is an organic substance called conchiolin, allied to the

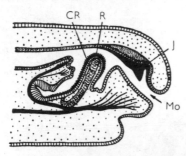

Figure 3. Diagrammatic vertical longitudinal section through
the buccal cavity and buccal
mass of a snail. CR Cartilage
supporting Radula, J Jaw, M
Mouth, R Radula.
(After Forcart.)

chitin of insects, which subsequently becomes impregnated with
lime (calcium carbonate).

So much, then, for the basic structure of the molluscs. Snails and
slugs belong to the Class Gastropoda, whose scientific name refers
to the fact that all its members "creep on their bellies". The whole
ventral surface of the gastropod body forms a continuous creeping
sole which is thrown into a series of tiny travelling waves of un-
dulation by the musculature of the foot.

The head is smoothly attached (no neck) to the front end of the
foot and bears one or two pairs of tentacles. A pair of simple eyes
are associated with one of these, either at the tips as shown in
Figures 1 and 2, or at the bases of the tentacles. The mouth is a
transverse slit underneath the anterior end of the head, just below
the first pair of tentacles, and leads into the buccal cavity (Figure 3)
—the first part of the alimentary canal, where food is ingested and
broken up. In the roof of the buccal cavity there is a small, fixed
jaw, while the floor is taken up by the buccal mass, a substantial
lump of cartilage and muscle which supports and works the radula
(Figure 4)—a narrow, strap-like, rasping tongue provided with a
great many transverse rows of flattened, tooth-like plates. The
preliminary "demolition" of the food is further assisted by the
mucus and enzymes secreted by the salivary glands, whose ducts

14

open into the buccal cavity even though they themselves lie well back alongside the crop. The buccal cavity leads by a narrow oesophagus into a broad crop, and thence onwards to the succeeding regions of the gut: the stomach, coiled intestine and, finally, the rectum and anus.

Part of the anterior gut of gastropods is accommodated as an intrusion into the upper part of the foot. Most of it, however, is contained within a finger-shaped bag—the visceral sac—growing out from the back of the animal, and this sac with its contained organs is known as the visceral mass. Now the gut often grows very much longer than the foot, and if the visceral hump were allowed to develop in a straight line it would become very cumbersome indeed and quite unwieldly when provided with a shell. In Gastropods, therefore, the visceral hump is coiled into a more compact spiral, varying from the plane spiral of the freshwater Ramshorn Snails (*Planorbis*) to the elongate spiral of the marine Towershells (*Turritella*). The spiral form of the shell is a consequence of the form of the visceral hump, and not *vice versa*, since, as we have already seen, the shell is secreted by the mantle, a glandular skin which covers and takes the form of the visceral hump. The degree of protection afforded by the shell to the visceral hump varies in different groups of snails, while in the slugs, whose general structure otherwise resembles that of the snails, the shell is reduced to a rudimentary cap or plate or lost altogether.

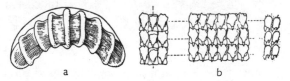

Figure 4. Jaw (a) and various types of teeth on the radula (b) of a Roman Snail, *Helix pomatia*. (After Forcart.)

A further complication is introduced by the phenomenon of "torsion" or twisting, in which the entire coil of the visceral hump is rotated through up to 180° about an axis perpendicular to the foot, with consequent disturbances of the symmetry and relationships of the viscera and associated nerve cords! As though this were not enough, a second group of gastropods have set about undoing this torsion while yet a third have retained the torsion and yet contrived a secondary return to symmetry in their nervous systems. All three groups (the Orders Prosobranchiata, Opisthobranchiata and Pulmonata, respectively) comprise "snails" in the popular sense, so that we have to be careful in giving a brief description of a generalised snail and, indeed, in our use of that very word.

Much of the bulk of the visceral hump is accounted for by the digestive gland, sometimes misnamed "liver", which secretes digestive juices into the crop, ingests small particles of food for subsequent digestion within itself and also stores nutritive material. The usually substantial size of this organ is quite understandable in the light of its threefold function.

The visceral hump also includes the reproductive organs. In hermaphrodite snails (those which combine both sexes in one

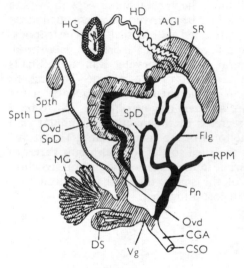

Figure 5. Dissection of the reproductive organs of a Roman Snail, *Helix pomatia*. Male parts shown black; female parts shaded; common sexual ducts white. AGl Albumen Gland, CGA Common Genital Atrium, CSO Common Sexual Opening, DS Dart Sac with enclosed Dart, Flg Flagellum, HD Hermaphrodite Duct, HG Hermaphrodite Gland (Ovotestis), MG Mucus Gland, Ovd Oviduct, Pn Penis, RPM Retractor Penis Muscle, SpD Sperm Duct, Spth Spermatheca (which dissolves spermatophores received from another snail), SpthD Spermathecal Duct, SR Seminal Receptacle (which stores sperm received from another snail and where fertilisation takes place), Vg Vagina. (After Forcart.)

individual) these form a complicated system based on an hermaphrodite gland (Figure 5); in those in which the sexes are separate there is a simpler arrangement with either an ovary or a testis.

The heart, enclosed in its bag or pericardium, likewise lies within the visceral hump, and close against it is the first part of the kidney whose cavity is confluent with the pericardial cavity through a narrow reno-pericardial canal. Externally the edge of the mantle is exposed as a sort of collar between the lip of the shell and the foot. There are also two external openings visible in this region. One, the smaller, is the anus—the terminal opening of the rectum or hindgut. The other leads into the respiratory chamber—part of the mantle-cavity contained between the mantle and the visceral hump —which contains the respiratory organ, either a lung (a network of capillary blood-vessels) or a gill as the case may be. The ureter, running down from the kidney, also discharges into the mantle-cavity quite close to the anus.

In the snail-like species which constitute the majority of gastropods all these vital internal organs are safely protected by the shell. Continuing protection is provided for by the growth of the shell which keeps pace with that of the animal's body by the accumulation of new shell-substance laid down around the shell-lip, secreted by the collar-like fold at the edge of the mantle. There glands of the mantle-fold secrete chitin-like conchiolin as a cuticle (the periostracum) covering the surface of the shell, while other glands produce a pasty, limy material which hardens to form the principal

Figure 6. Shell of a Roman Snail, *Helix pomatia*, sawn across to expose the axis or columella (seen through the opening).

layer (the ostracum) which gives the snail-shell the necessary strength and solidity. Growth does not proceed uninterruptedly but in sections, demarcated by fine furrows parallel to the edge of the lip; the intervening zones are called growth-bands. Deeper grooves are formed in the surface of the shell when there are longer interruptions of growth, perhaps as a consequence of winter or of a dry season.

The majority of snail-shells are such a generous fit that the animals can retire from public life by withdrawing their whole bodies into them. This withdrawal is effected by the strong, branching columella muscle which is attached along one edge to the axis, or columella, of the shell (Figure 6) and on the other side pulls upon various portions of the trunk. In operculate snails, which in the retired condition close the mouths of their shells with a lid, or operculum, perched on the hind end of the foot, the columella also sends a strong branch to this structure.

In water-snails the principal function of the shell is to protect the soft body from enemies; in land-snails, however, it has another and equally important one. The snail's skin is only a thin, soft, stratified cell-layer with hardly any resistance to evaporation. The secretion of slime from the many glands in this skin is insufficient as a counter-measure to dry-season conditions, when only complete withdrawal within the shell affords adequate protection against life-threatening loss of water. Then, to make assurance doubly sure, the snail secretes one or more slime-membranes which dry and seal off the mouth of the shell (Plate 4).

The snail's nervous system consists of several pairs of nerve-knots (ganglia), interconnected by transverse and longitudinal nerve-strands. It is, in fact, a largely decentralised nervous system whose separate ganglia serve adjacent regions and organ-systems of the body—head, foot, visceral mass, etc. This "scatter-brained" condition has evidently imposed a serious limitation upon the evolutionary potentialities of the gastropods, for we find in the highest molluscs, the cephalopods (octupuses, squids and their relatives), that concentration of the nervous ganglia into what can only be described as a true "brain" has made much more complicated behaviour-patterns possible.

The sense-organs of gastropods are simple in structure. Cephalic tentacles and lips subserve the sense of taste; the pimple-eyes discriminate between light and dark and convey impressions of form; gilled water-snails have an olfactory organ (osphradium) inside the mantle cavity; in land-snails the tentacles, mouth-parts and anterior margin of the foot perceive chemical stimuli. The whole skin is sensitive to chemical and mechanical stimuli.

Animal groups are not only characterised by peculiarities of their internal and external structure; they also have biological peculiarities in such processes, for example, as reproduction and development. We have already seen that gastropods include both hermaphrodite (sexes combined) and heterosexual (sexes distinct) species. In the gastropod realm generally these two types are about evenly balanced, but in the British land and freshwater gastropods which are our immediate interest, including a high-proportion of lung-breathing snails (Pulmonata), hermaphrodite species greatly predominate. In our fauna only the few front-gilled snails (Prosobranchia) have separate sexes. In these cases there are males with a testis producing sperm and females with an ovary producing eggs; sperm enter the female's body during pairing and fertilise the eggs which, as a rule, are subsequently laid in chains.

In the hermaphrodite species we find really intricate relations in the structure of the reproductive organs and in the process of mating. Each individual produces both eggs and sperm in an hermaphrodite gland (ovotestis). The sperm and eggs ripen at different times and are led away through the hermaphrodite duct

(Figure 5). For some distance beyond this the cavities of the sperm duct and oviduct are in lateral communication with one another but eventually the sperm duct breaks away as a separate tube leading to a muscular penis. In some species the sperm are formed into a packet or spermatophore. Eventually there is a reciprocal exchange of spermatophores or fluid semen during mating with another snail.

The eggs likewise develop in the hermaphrodite gland and pass along the hermaphrodite duct to await fertilisation in a pocket—the seminal receptacle—at the entrance to the albumen gland which provides them with certain nutritive substances essential to their further development.

There is sometimes quite an elaborate pattern of courtship behaviour, easily studied in the Roman Snail (*Helix pomatia*) or the commoner Garden Snail (*H. aspersa*). These species secrete a harpoon-like calcareous love-dart in a glandular outgrowth from the lower end of the oviduct, and as their love-making approaches its climax there is a reciprocal ejection of darts deep into the body of the partner. Eventually the snails approach one another, each everting its penis through its common sexual opening and inserting it into the vagina of the partner, there is a mutual exchange of spermatophores, and the partners separate and go their separate ways (*see also* p. 164).

Further developments are just as remarkable, for the stranger sperm do not at once proceed up the oviduct to where the eggs await them. Instead they first pass through the spermathecal duct to the spermatheca, where the covering of the spermatophore is dissolved away and the sperm may remain for a while. Then they make their way back down the spermathecal duct to its junction with the oviduct, and up the oviduct to the seminal receptacle where they fertilise the eggs. The fertilised eggs descend the oviduct, receiving mucus secretions and sometimes a shell on the way, and are eventually laid through the common sexual opening.

Having thus made the acquaintance of the snails and slugs we turn to a like consideration of the mussels and their relatives. It is best to study them in rather greater detail, since they do not lend themselves so well to later personal observations.

In comparison with snails, mussels present many modifications in body-form and internal structure (Figures 7 and 8). Even the many scientific names applied to their class provide indications of these: they have been called Acephala ("headless ones"), Pelecypoda ("hatchet-footed ones"), Lamellibranchiata ("leaf-gilled ones"), Conchifera ("shell-bearers") and Bivalvia ("two-valved ones").

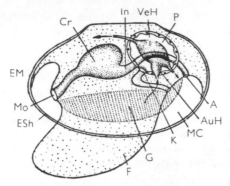

Figure 7. Schematic diagram of the structure of a generalised mussel. A Anus, AuH Auricle of Heart, Cr Crop, EM Edge of Mantle, ESh Edge of Shell, F Foot, G Gill, In Intestine, K Kidney, MC Mantle Cavity, Mo Mouth, P Pericardium, VeH Ventricle of Heart. (After Kühn.)

All mussels have a shell which differs from that of the snails in being composed of two halves or valves, and as a rule the two valves are symmetrical mirror-images of one another. Disparities arise chiefly in cases like the marine oyster where the animal attaches itself by one valve. Along a long edge, the dorsal one, the two valves are united by an elastic band—the hinge-ligament. In this region the shell-margins of most species exhibit alternate tooth-like elevations and depressions which interlock (Figure 9). These contrivances, called hinges, prevent the displacement of one valve upon

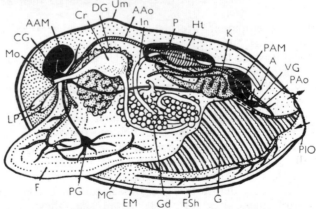

Figure 8. Internal structure of a mussel after removal of the shell-valve and some of the organs of the left side. A Anus, AAM Anterior Adductor Muscle, AAo Anterior Aorta, CG Cerebral Ganglion, Cr Crop, DG Digestive Gland ("Liver"), EM Edge of Mantle, EO Exhalant Opening, ESh Edge of Shell, F Foot, G Gill, Gd Gonad (ovary or testis), Ht Heart, In Intestine, K Kidney, LP Labial Palps, MC Mantle Cavity, Mo Mouth, P Pericardium, PAM Posterior Adductor Muscle, PAo Posterior Aorta, PG Pedal Ganglion, PIO Papillae around Inhalant Opening, Um Umbo, VG Visceral Ganglion.

20

another. Since the hinge-teeth are differently constructed in different species, they also provide us with useful characters for species-recognition.

The animal can close its shell very firmly by means of one or two stout adductor muscles which extend transversely between the insides of the valves. The insertions, or places of attachment, of these muscles are recognisable in empty shells, since their scars take the form of smooth areas or depressions which vary from species to species and accordingly provide us with further identification characters. The adductor muscles are the antagonists of the hinge-ligament which, in the absence of muscular tension, forces the valves open (*see also* p. 136).

Figure 9. Interior of left shell-valve of a Painter's Mussel, *Unio pictorum*. The uppermost elevation is the umbo, and the stout, serrated projection below it is the cardinal tooth of the hinge. From the latter the ledge-like lateral teeth extend on either side. The shaded areas on the right and left are the scars, or depressed insertion-surfaces, of the anterior and posterior adductor muscles respectively (*see also* p. 136).

We have already learned something about the structure of the snail's shell. Mussel-shells are likewise composed of several layers. On the outside we recognise the cuticle of conchiolin—the periostracum—which is usually brown in freshwater mussels. If this is removed, as indeed it often is under natural conditions, the white, calcareous middle layer—the ostracum—is exposed. Below this again, in contrast to the great majority of snail-shells, there is a third layer, of mother-of-pearl, although in most cases this merely takes the form of a porcelain-like layer. (The iridescence of mother-of-pearl is due to its prismatic structure which diffracts light; the same material laid down in any other form appears merely grey or dead white.)

As a rule, the whole of the soft body of the animal is accommodated between the valves of the shell. The moderate trunk, which contains the viscera, fills the dorsal part of the shell. The middle part of the trunk extends ventrally into the foot, which is usually shaped like a hatchet-head (Figure 10). The foot can be protruded between the open valves of the shell and is used for locomotion and for digging.

21

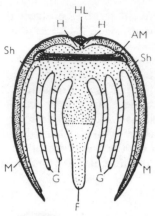

Figure 10. Diagrammatic transverse section through a mussel. AM Adductor Muscle, F Foot, G Gills, H Hinge, HL Hinge-Ligament, M Mantle, Sh Shell.

The pair of shell valves is apposed internally to skin-like folds which extend from the sides of the trunk. These form the mantle, whose outermost richly glandular layer lays down the substance of the shell. They are also responsible for the formation of pearls, for when a grain of sand, a parasite or some other small object intrudes between the shell and the mantle, the mantle can envelop the foreign body. In this "pearl-pouch" mother-of-pearl is laid down about the object and it becomes a free pearl. Often, however, the mantle tissue does not completely enclose it, and the result is only a pearl accretion connected to the shell which is then quite worthless.

On either side of the body are spaces between the mantle and the foot which constitute the mussel's mantle-cavities, corresponding to the undivided mantle-cavity in the snails, and which contain the respiratory organs. Since mussels are, without exception, aquatic animals, these are always gills (Figure 10). One pair of gills is suspended in each mantle-cavity and, since the individual filaments coalesce with one another, they usually appear leaf-shaped.

The generally valid proposition, already tested in the snails, that the front end of an animal is where the head is, is inconclusive when applied to mussels; mussels have no head! If we want to distinguish front from rear in a living mussel we have to look for the hinder end. Here the close approximation or even coalescence of the edges of the mantle is interrupted to leave two slit-like openings, which in burrowing bivalves are often produced into long tubes or siphons. The lower or ventral opening, surrounded by taste-buds, or papillae, is the inhalant opening. Through this opening, drawn by ciliary action, water flows in over the gills, yielding up its oxygen and becoming laden with carbon dioxide until it is brought to a halt in

22

front of the mouth. This also lies within the shell and even in front of the foot and of the obvious opening on the opposite side. Labial palps, one on either side, strain off small food-particles from the water, entangle them in mucus, and carry them by ciliary action towards the mouth. The water is now carried backwards and, mixed with excreta from the anus and kidney, leaves the mussel through the upper, or dorsal, slit-like opening already noted—the exhalant opening.

Food ingested through the mouth passes straight through a short oesophagus into a spacious crop without being previously disintegrated. In contrast to snails, mussels have no jaw, radula or other mouth-parts. The sensory papillae around the inhalant opening sample the incoming food-particles and "turn the tap off" to prevent any large fragments entering the mouth or even entering the gill-chamber, so that only fine and palatable food arrives at the mouth and mouth-parts are rendered superfluous! A large digestive gland is associated with the crop and, as in snails, secretes digestive juices, takes up digested food and stores it.

At the junction of the crop and the gut we find an organ which is peculiar to the bivalves and a few gastropods, the crystalline style. This is a gelatinous rod of solidified gut-secretion whose distal end projects into the crop where it is continually dissolved while its proximal end rotates in a sac which continually secretes new material. The crystalline style is a mixture of a protein with an enzyme which breaks down carbohydrates; it appears to serve as a reserve food-store as well as for digestion.

The food continues, following the many windings of the intestine, until it reaches the anus which lies near the exhalant opening. Part of the intestinal coil also extends into the foot. A singular peculiarity of mussel anatomy is the fact that the hind-gut passes through the pericardial sac of the posteriorly situated heart, and the heart itself is wrapped around the gut. The anterior part of the kidney arises from the pericardium, as in snails. The kidney itself is a bag-like tube which discharges into the mantle-cavity. The connection between the cavities of the pericardium and kidney in molluscs shows that these are the remains of a true primitive body-cavity or coelom.

The mussel's nervous system is symmetrically constructed as in most animals and unlike the majority of gastropods. It appears very simple as a result of the close approximation of the nerve-ganglia and comprises three pairs of large ganglia: the coalesced cerebral ganglia before and above the mouth, the pedal ganglia anteriorly in the foot and the visceral ganglia. In addition to supplying the principal organs of the body they are connected with numerous sensory organs chiefly concerned with the perception of chemical and mechanical stimuli. As a curiosity it may be noted that some bivalves, such as the Scallops (*Pecten*), possess eyes despite their headlessness. These are simple light sense-organs at the edges of the mantle, corresponding to the head-eyes of gastropods, but in no way comparable with the magnificently elaborated eyes of cephalopods which, indeed, rival those of vertebrates.

While the underlying common denominators of molluscan structure should by now be evident from our comparison of the

Figure 11. *Glochidium* larva of
a freshwater mussel.

two groups, the mussels have shown us several striking differences between their build and ground-plan and those of the snails. We shall now see further divergences in their biology, especially as regards the reproduction and development of many groups of freshwater mussels.

In general it can be said that the majority of all bivalve species have separate sexes, and that the gonads (ovaries or testes) producing eggs or sperm are accommodated in different individuals. The gonads in mussels lie between the gut-coil and the mouth, close by the opening of the kidney and thus anterior to the exhalant opening. The hermaphrodite species have an hermaphrodite gland which produces eggs and sperm either simultaneously or successively. The sperm are discharged into the water in vast numbers through the exhalant opening, but only a tiny fraction of them reach the inhalant respiratory streams of other mussels. If the latter are females or hermaphrodites with eggs, fertilisation takes place; if they are males, of course, there is simply a further waste of sperm.

Marine bivalves expel their fertilised eggs into the open sea where they develop into planktonic larvae; so also do the freshwater Zebra Mussels (Dreissenidae). Some freshwater mussels, on the other hand, practise brood-care. In the hermaphrodite Orb-shells (Sphaeriidae) the fertilised eggs develop into young animals in the gill brood-pouches. The brood of the separate-sexed River Mussels (Unionidae), on the other hand, have a more complicated development. The eggs at first become embedded in the gills where they

24

develop as far as a mussel-like larval stage, the *Glochidium* (Figure 11). The glochidia are expelled from the mother animal into the open water. Further development requires a fish as host-animal, on whose gills or skin the glochidia then prosper. There they become overgrown by gill-membrane or skin and in the cysts so formed they grow up and become transformed into young mussels. One day the investing skin bursts open and the baby mussels are released. All glochidia, however, which do not succeed in reaching a fish— and that means the great majority—fall to the bottom. It is quite extraordinary that at least one fish has succeeded in obtaining its revenge on the mussels. The Bitterling (*Rhodeus amarus*), a member of the carp family, lays its eggs in a Freshwater Mussel (*Unio* or *Anodonta*) and thus uses the mussel as a nursery for its own brood!

Part Two

Planning a Collection

Once you become fully aware of snails and other molluscs and begin to keep a look out, it is surprising how frequently you meet with them. Moreover, in many places you will come across empty snail- and mussel-shells and, when these several finds are compared with one another, new ones, not previously discovered, are brought to light. Obviously there are quite a lot of different species, some of them large, others quite tiny. But it is impossible to develop a practised eye merely by profiting from the chance individual find. A satisfactory knowledge of our native mollusc fauna is best obtained by methodical collecting.

The collection of objects of natural history should never be undertaken merely to fulfil a vague and purposeless impulse to collect. The aim is to bring together all the different snail- and mussel-shells you can find in order to obtain a picture of the species occurring in a definite district. The collecting area is only extended further when all the prerequisites, such as time, energy and storage-space for the collection, permit such extension beyond home environs. Incomplete statements regarding the molluscs of a large area are far less significant than a thorough investigation of a small district!

A second purpose of collection should be to learn to distinguish the different species and to determine them correctly. Here it should be clearly understood and acknowledged that in most cases only full-grown snails lend themselves to certain identification. You will soon learn to tell the difference between an immature and a completed shell-mouth, and therefore be able to distinguish a young animal from an adult (*see* p. 49). Later, perhaps, you may start a special collection of young snails' shells, including all stages of development, from which you will be able to say quite positively to which species any unknown one belongs. That will help, too, in cases where a young snail is the only representative of its species in the collection.

The third important purpose of a collection is to enable the collector to gain knowledge of the living-conditions and natural habitats of snails and mussels. This requires especially meticulous observation and involves making a critical study of the spot where the animal is collected and writing down all the particulars of that situation.

However, there is a responsibility attached to collecting: never to give way to a sheer passion for collecting by taking more than a few specimens. This admonition only applies to living animals, of course, but it is a very serious one and well founded. In these over-crowded islands of ours, with more and more of the countryside being taken up by building, industrial needs and more modern methods of cultivation and fencing, the truly wild places are shrinking fast and many animals, molluscs among them, are becoming restricted to a few, often quite small, localities. They could easily become extinct altogether as the result of immoderate collecting. Empty shells, on the other hand, are quite a different matter; you can console yourself by stuffing all your pockets with them!

Nevertheless, a true collector never puts snails and mussels directly into his pockets. On his excursions he carries an adequate stock of well-plugged glass or plastic tubes—the patent medicine industry keeps us well provided with those—and tin boxes of various sizes. Cardboard boxes are not suitable and, at most, should only be used for the transport of empty shells on occasion. Living animals turn the cardboard into a pulp with their slime and then eat their way out.

For the transport of freshwater snails or mussels these containers should be packed with damp moss or water-plants. Actual transport in water is not necessary since the animals can spend long periods in the retired condition and only emerge when it is wet. In every case, too, the collector must take particular care not to mix up the specimens from different localities; each new discovery requires and gets a fresh container. And if you find small, delicate species and large, thick-shelled ones at one and the same site, you should again provide separate containers for them so as not to damage the more fragile animals.

As you pack your specimens, write numbers on the stoppers or lids of their containers in a sequence corresponding to the sequence of sites at which they were collected. At the same time, in a note-book or scribbling pad, enter after each corresponding number the name of the site or a sketch-map showing its position in regard to more certainly identifiable reference-points. Next, add the date and other particulars and give a brief caption-like description of the specimens' habitat. This will simplify sorting when you return home.

A typical entry might look like the following example:

> 3. *Sunhill, 200 yds. north of the road from A-village to B-village near the "steep hill" sign. Sunhill slopes due south; dry, warm position. Plants: chicory, stinging nettles, plantain.*

Another good idea is to acquire the 1-in. ordnance survey map of the district being collected and learn to indicate the position of sites by the appropriate National Grid reference; "Sunhill, 509 356" would fix the position within less than 100 yds., and all you have to do is to estimate that it lies nine-tenths of the way between the numbered co-ordinates 50 and 51 and six-tenths of the way between co-ordinates 35 and 36 on the map.

Having brought home a rich haul of treasures, the next stage is the preparation of the specimens collected, to make them ready for incorporation into the shell collection. In the case of empty shells this process is relatively simple. If they are dirty inside and out, as is almost always the case, soften the dirt by soaking them in water, making sure that the snail-shells are filled with water so that they sink. If the shells are reasonably robust this can be done by putting them in a fruit-bowl or large jam-jar and moving the vessel in a circle as it is filled under the tap. But delicate shells are best treated individually under a fine jet of water, being rotated between the fingers and filled until they overflow. It is important to make sure that the water penetrates right inside the shell and that no air-bubbles are trapped inside the last part of the whorl. The shells should remain immersed in water for from two to four days in order to loosen the dried remains of their soft parts as well. Next, let a strong jet of water spurt into the vessel for a few minutes until the overspill runs clear. The dirt residue can then be removed by repeated changes of water. In particularly stubborn cases it helps if the shell is flushed out by aiming a syringe directly into the mouth. After softening, surface dirt is soon removed by cautious brushing with a soft toothbrush but this requires very great care in the case of hairy species, whose hair should be preserved if at all possible. Shells thus cleaned should then be left to dry, protected from sunshine and dust and preferably covered with wire gauze to keep away egg-laying flies.

If you have collected living animals they must first be killed. There are several ways of doing this; one is to pour boiling water over them. But this short heat-treatment is not sufficient for large operculate snails or large mussels which require to be boiled for several minutes. The next stage is the removal of the soft parts. As a rule this presents no difficulty in mussels and can readily be achieved by simple scratching and scraping. To prevent the cleaned mussel-shells from gaping open they must be bound around with strong twine, which can be removed once they are dry. If, later on, you want to open the shells again for the purpose of studying them, you need only soften the hinge-ligaments in water. If possible duplicate specimens should be preserved in the open condition.

The procedure involved in preparing snails is not quite so easy. To begin with, select the species in which, in consequence of their

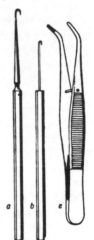

Figure 12. Instruments required for preparing specimens. a Hooked dissecting needle, b Hooked entomological needle with handle, c Curved forceps.

small size, narrow mouths, mouth-folds, etc., mechanical removal of the soft parts is impossible. After killing the animals, leave them to rot ("macerate" is the correct technical term) in water for several days until you can rid the shells of their soft parts by agitation or syringing as described previously for empty shells. The maceration procedure should not be too prolonged, however, since in time the cuticle of the shell (which includes an organic substance) also begins to decompose.

In the case of large snails with normal mouths, the soft bodies can be removed as soon as the water used in killing them has cooled. Depending on the size of the animals you will require a pair of forceps (preferably with curved ends), a dissecting needle with a hooked point, a hooked entomological needle or suitably bent wires which look less professional but serve equally well (Figure 12). Insert the instrument into the body, preferably in such a manner that as many structures as possible are transfixed so as to minimise the risk of a portion tearing away. Then, rotating the shell in relation to the coil and at the same time pulling carefully on the soft body, attempt to bring the whole animal out of the shell in one piece. This requires a neat, practised action however and you may not always succeed in your early attempts, above all because part of the digestive gland is very liable to be left behind. On the other hand, however, there are some species in which fragments of the soft parts always get left behind in the shell. In such cases, and wherever ordinary manipulative methods prove inadequate, it helps if the specimens are given a macerative treatment as described for empty shells.

Where there is an operculum present this should be separated from the hind end of the foot, cleaned and placed inside the mouth of the dried shell. The mouth is then plugged with cotton wool so that the shell and corresponding operculum always remain together. Alternatively, you can fit a plug of cotton wool into the mouth of the shell first and then replace the operculum so that it fits over the mouth as in the living animal.

If you have slugs among your newly collected specimens, aim to keep the whole soft body in as natural a condition as possible. This requires two distinct stages, technically known as fixation and preservation. Fixation is the process whereby the animal is killed in such a fashion that not only the natural extended position of the body is retained, with the minimum of bloating or shrinkage, but also even the microscopic structure of the tissues is retained as near as possible as in life. Preservation, the subsequent process, is the means by which decay or other subsequent deterioration of the specimen is prevented.

Commence by putting the animals in a vessel with a level edge, which has been filled to the brim with boiled water (boiled to drive off as much as possible of the dissolved oxygen and also to sterilise the water). Then add a few drops of a 1% aqueous solution of chloral hydrate to the water and carefully slide a glass plate over the top of the vessel in such a way that no air-bubbles remain trapped underneath it. For safety, weight the glass plate with a stone or a heavy paperweight. By this method the animals are first narcotised and then die in an extended position. The exact moment when you can remove the animals is something which you must decide for yourself in any particular case; usually it is a matter of anything between several hours and a day later.

Having killed the animals, clean them with a soft brush under running water in order to rid them of adhering slime, and then transfer them to 50% alcohol (*see* p. 31). Three days later, transfer them to 70% and after a further three days to 80% alcohol in which they then remain. The purpose of these operations is to actually replace most of the water in the animals' bodies with alcohol and to do this gradually so that the specimens do not become shrunken and hard.

Earlier we mentioned the process of fixation: while it is true that the specimens are eventually fixed after a fashion by the method just described, and well enough to serve as entire museum specimens, a zoologist wanting material for microscopic examination would use a more exacting technique. Another point is that the purchase of absolute alcohol or industrial methylated spirits for scientific purposes in Great Britain requires a permit from the local Customs and Excise Office. Young specialists wishing to obtain one would be well advised to consult their science teacher first. The purple commercial methylated spirit which can be bought without a permit is unfortunately useless for our purposes.

When arranging a collection, unidentified shells from widely separated localities must be carefully segregated. Glass or plastic specimen tubes or boxes of various sizes are suitable for this, the tubes being closed with a plug of cotton wool, a cork, or a plastic cap, and the boxes with reliable elastic bands or strong twine. Every experienced collector knows how often and how easily specimens collected can mysteriously "change" their localities of origin. A postage stamp tells us whether it came from Germany or Switzerland, but a Roman Snail keeps its own counsel! So, from the very outset, no trouble is too great to be worth taking to prevent errors of this kind. In particular, then, remember to transcribe the locality data from your notebooks onto small labels (good rag paper and reliable ink, especially when they have to be immersed in spirit!) and put them inside the specimen containers. Now any expert, whether yourself or a stranger, can really make something of your specimens.

When both shells and preserved animals have been identified, write labels for the individual species. These should be about 2 in. by ½ in. in size, permanent as regards paper and writing, and laid out on the lines of the following model:

Roman Snail (*Helix pomatia* L.)
Dry, southerly slope of Sunhill,
1 mile north-east of A-village, Someshire;
30.8.1964; John Smith, collector.

Provided you preserve your records, and it is highly desirable that you should, all the other data can be omitted; otherwise, enter them briefly on the back of the label.

Each species from each locality should be stored in its own individual container. For this purpose it is an advantage to have specimen tubes of standard sizes and likewise cardboard or plastic boxes, preferably with transparent tops. Only thus can the collection make an orderly and inspiring impression in a drawer. Tubes (Figure 13) are used for small- and medium-sized species; boxes are employed chiefly for the larger ones. So that they will be freely interchangeable in the collection you should obtain them in the following sizes:

Glass or plastic specimen tubes with a standard length of 3 in. and diameters of $\frac{1}{2}$, $\frac{3}{4}$, 1 and $1\frac{1}{2}$ in.

Cardboard boxes with glass tops (or transparent plastic ones) of the following dimensions (length × breadth × depth in inches in each case): $3 \times 3 \times 1\frac{1}{2}$; $4 \times 3 \times 2$; $6 \times 3 \times 2$.

Then when rearrangement of the collection is necessary you can always move, exchange and transfer the tubes and boxes without having to remove their contents (Figure 14). This has the particular advantage that the species label with the vital locality data is not unnecessarily exposed to the danger of loss or interchange.

Slugs, preserved in alcohol, must be stored separately. They are put, still in 80% alcohol, in small upright jars about 6 in. high and $2\frac{1}{2}$ in. in diameter (Figure 13a) and provided with two species labels, one inside with the specimen and a duplicate stuck onto the outside of the jar. The one immersed in spirit, especially, should be

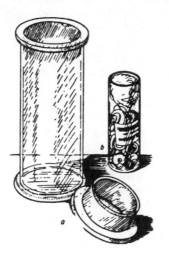

Figure 13. Specimen containers. a Upright museum jar with ground-glass stopper, used for material preserved in spirit, b Specimen tube used for empty shells.

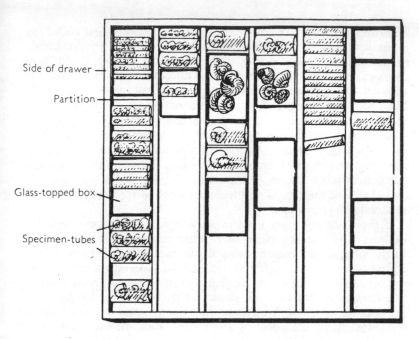

Side of drawer

Partition

Glass-topped box

Specimen-tubes

Figure 14. Example of a drawer from a shell collection.

written on a good rag paper (not wood-pulp) and preferably with a good waterproof black drawing-ink which has been tested for reliability and allowed to dry thoroughly before immersion. The spirit collection should always be kept in the dark in order to minimise the fading of the colours, although unfortunately alcohol itself destroys many of them. (The recently developed techniques of embedding natural history specimens in blocks of transparent plastic have achieved some striking successes in preserving the colours, and amateur kits are on sale already in the United States although they are not as easily come by in this country.) Pure ethyl alcohol is very expensive, so use industrial methyl alcohol "for scientific purposes" (*see above*) but *not* commercial methylated spirits. Iso-propyl alcohol is also very good value. The 80% alcohol in the specimen jars needs "topping-up" from time to time because there is always some evaporation however tightly the jars are stoppered.

Collecting Begins

Having acquired a good knowledge of the distinguishing characters, preparation and curation of the snails, slugs and mussels to

33

be brought in, you are now ready to set out on your first collecting excursion. Again, however, this must be preceded by systematic planning so as to ensure the greatest possible success. Profit from the accumulated experience of other collectors and benefit from the tricks which they have devised to facilitate collecting.

Land Snails and Slugs A point fundamental to the collecting of land molluscs is the fact that they are damp atmosphere animals. Accordingly, you can always bargain on success when you start out in wet weather, after a shower or thunderstorm, or early in the morning, or from late evening to dewfall. These are the times and conditions when snails feel in their element and when you can expect to find the typical resident species of each locality abroad in relatively large crowds.

If there has not been a recent shower or thunderstorm, you will do best if you search places which are certain to be damp. Such likely habitats are marshes and damp meadows, banks of watercourses and ponds, sheltered defiles, and especially such as have springs, tussocks of moss, dead leaves, tree-stumps, rotten wood, tree-bark and thickets of dense vegetation. Tree-trunks, too, harbour many species which crawl up them during wet weather and then, caught by the onset of a dry spell, stick themselves on with their slime and retire into their shells to await the next rains.

Obviously, you can also collect successfully in places which are not particularly damp, even in dry ones, but they are tenanted by quite a different group of species. Thus you will appreciate the concept of the ecological niche, the expression which zoologists apply to the combination of living conditions and mode of life to which individual species become adapted and specialised in their structure and behaviour. Rocks, walls and ruins are in the front rank of such likely finding-places. If you are not content with the empty shells lying around, you can search under moss, grass, humus and in crevices and cracks in walls for the few snails which have retired there before the drought came. In dry seasons snails may also be found under large, loose stones, so take the trouble to turn these over, not forgetting that here, as even more on the seashore, the good collector always replaces each stone in its original position after he has finished his search. The life of land molluscs is far more effectively suited to all these sites than it is to conditions elsewhere.

Large quantities of empty shells, mainly of the smaller species, can be found amongst the rubbish brought down by streams and rivers and accordingly it is worth while to sort over the plant débris of all kinds deposited along the flood-line of a river bank. Many dead insects are to be found here as well as snail-shells. Of course,

34

in this case, the locality of origin does not correspond to the place where the shell is found, yet it will tell you that the species lives along the banks somewhere upstream. And after all, water-transport extends the distribution areas of many species.

Molehills offer likely possibilities of finding empty shells, especially those of small, soil-dwelling species.

If you search the right places at the right times, then, you will probably be sure of getting a good haul. However, when you survey the results of the first few excursions it may strike you that we have obtained hardly any shells less than about ¼ in. high or broad. Probably there are only a few small species? Far from it! The reason is in our own eyes which, amid the general confusion of vegetation, soil and stones, are liable to overlook snails beneath a certain size. Small species, too, are specially favoured because, living as they do, close to the ground, in humus or moss or even in the soil, the majority are liable to escape our notice.

You can, however, remedy this deficiency by applying suitable collecting methods, and in particular by enlisting the help of a series of simple tools. In the first place, provide yourself with a small rake-cum-trowel about a foot in length as used for window-box cultivation (Figure 15)—a double-ended implement which is used for

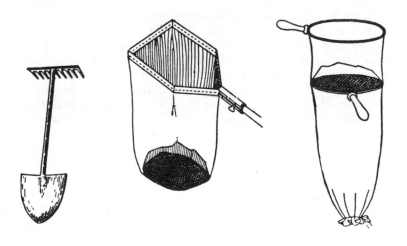

Figure 15. Rake-cum-trowel.

Figure 16. Fishing-net (part cut away to show the bottom).

Figure 17. Sieve-bag (part cut away to show the sieve-plate).

scratching the surface of the soil, raking apart fallen leaves and humus, breaking up molehills and general rummaging around. In this way you will secure many a species which would otherwise have eluded you.

Another indispensable piece of equipment is the fishing-net (Figure 16), which should be made from coarse, close-meshed material and is used for sweeping through undergrowth and herbage. It is also useful in collecting water-snails.

In conclusion, you need a sieve-bag (Figure 17), in which you can shake dead leaves, moss and rubbish. The material which falls through the sieve (about $\frac{1}{2}$ in. mesh) is put into bags and sorted through at home. If you cannot obtain a sieve-bag or make one for yourself, a deep-sided sieve will do just as well, the material being allowed to fall through onto a sheet of cloth or paper and then put into bags as before.

The sifted material should be allowed to dry before examination, then spread it out, remove the coarser foreign matter and throw the residue into a bowl of water. As the water is thoroughly stirred, the material begins to sort itself out; sand, earth and small stones fall to the bottom while plant debris and snails float to the surface. Occasionally some of the snails sink as well, but they lie on top of the mineral component and are easily skimmed off.

Plant remains and snails must now be allowed to dry out again, then the mixture is put into a dish, a little at a time, and carefully blown upon. Thus we separate "the chaff from the wheat" as the saying goes, the "wheat" in this case being the snails which, since they are heavier, are left behind in the dish. If the sifted mixture contains little or no mineral component in the first place then you can proceed directly to blowing off the plant detritus as soon as it has been dried. Finally, sort the snails according to size and again according to kind, put them into small glass containers and label them.

Another method of working out sifted material requires the use of a further series of sieves with gradually diminishing meshes of about $\frac{1}{5}$, $\frac{1}{10}$ and $\frac{1}{20}$ in. (5, 2–3 and 1 mm.). This yields portions with snails and foreign particles of approximately similar size which must then be separated from one another by blowing, sorting, etc.

Apart from sifting out dead leaves, moss, humus and so on, there are further methods which are specially favourable to the capture of small species. Sometimes it is possible to stir up or cut up plants and scatter them in water. Again, we can pile up heaps of coarse plant-fragments, search through them and shake them out from time to time. Scythed grass and weeds, piled into little heaps, will yield many species which otherwise would elude the collector.

Finally, a further word about the most favourable time of year for collecting. Apart from a hard winter with much snow and deep frost, collecting can continue throughout the year, but spring is the best season and then, after a warm shower, you can expect to come upon whole swarms of snails in the right locality. Summer is less favourable because then many snails are concealed by dense vegetation and, on the other hand, many hide themselves away to escape the prevalent droughts. At this season sifting is the most likely method of obtaining a good haul. In autumn conditions become more favourable to collecting and this also is the time when we find the largest proportion of full-grown animals. In winter there will always be empty shells to be found where the ground is free from snow. To obtain the species which only creep around in winter you must first obtain an accurate knowledge of their habitats; the same applies when you want to root out snails from their winter quarters. Small snails can be captured in wintertime by bringing home samples of soil and laying them in a warm place so as to induce the animals present therein to creep out and show themselves. Fresh molehills, also, are veritable specimen-mines in winter. Thus, there need be no slack time to collecting throughout the whole year.

Freshwater Snails and Mussels Freshwater molluscs should be represented in any collection even though they are sometimes rather more troublesome to capture than land snails. You can avoid much unpleasantness by providing yourself with suitably strong and weatherproof clothing. Footwear is especially important when collecting aquatic animals, since not everyone enjoys continually getting his feet wet. Waterproof footwear, preferably a pair of gum-boots, is the best foundation for collecting trips. (And in the translator's experience, wet feet or no wet feet, it is better to keep at least an old pair of plimsolls or gym-shoes for any kind of paddling; there are too many broken bottles and old cans around in even the remotest places nowadays and a gashed foot, very likely in dirty water and miles from home, is a much greater inconvenience than carrying a pair of wet shoes in a plastic bag.)

In the water, as on land, not every habitat is a "snaily" one. Substantial populations of snails and mussels are always to be found in slow-flowing or stagnant waters—such as river backwaters, lakes, ponds and ditches, especially when they provide a rich growth of water-weeds. Such waters occur chiefly in the lowland plains; hill streams, with their swift flow and scanty plant-growth, do not suit the majority of snails and mussels and harbour only a minority of specially adapted species, such as the freshwater limpet (*Ancylus*) which usually lives on or under stones.

We are always astonished at the meagre mollusc faunas of high peat-bogs. Such waters are usually stained brown by humic acids and are very poor in nutrients. In consequence, the aquatic vegetation in them is poor and often lacking in the snails' principal food-plants so that even when snails are present at all they are usually stunted in their growth. Their lack of lime is a further important factor.

How does the collector set about his task by and in waters which appear to be promising? Collecting is undoubtedly simplest along the shores of lakes, where it is possible to examine the wave-wash zone and the inshore shallows, chiefly in search of empty shells. In ponds and waterholes you can net the plants and drag the upper layer of the mud, rinsing the proceeds in the fishing-net in either case because there is no point in carrying home redundant mud. Likewise in rivers you can wade in the shallows, running the net through the mud and weeds. It is also very worth while to lift out as many stones as possible and thoroughly scrutinise all their surfaces in the hand. The techniques applied to the shallows of rivers can be applied across the whole breadth of smaller streams. Here special attention should be paid to the possibility of large mussels being present embedded in the bottom, since these, of course, only expose small portions of themselves.

In the absence of a boat, collecting in lakes is confined to the marginal regions; a boat, however, opens up greater possibilities. Once again the net can be used to bring up weeds and surface mud from the bottom. If the plant growth reaches near enough to the surface, you can pull in handfuls intact and rinse them in a basin, when any snails present will collect on the bottom. If there is good enough visibility to the bottom, try to fish up mussels with a long-handled rake. The same applies to ponds.

If you can gain access to a fishpond when it is drained, you then have a unique opportunity to scour the entire bottom. This is an especially good way to obtain a rich haul of mussels. (Such opportunities are rare in Britain because fishponds are not very common. There are compensating possibilities, however. The translator remembers, as a boy, collecting all the British species of *Unio*, *Anodonta*, *Dreissena* and *Paludina* in one afternoon when he found the double locks on the Exeter Canal drained. Likewise a mill-leat near his home used to be emptied every year for cleaning, and this provided several species of *Sphaerium* and *Pisidium* together with many other interesting animals. The spoil from canal dredgers also afforded numerous deepwater species.)

The best results can be expected from collecting freshwater snails and mussels all the way from spring through to autumn. In winter, on the other hand, the majority of species retire to considerable depths of water or into the mud on the bottom, where they are usually safe from our clutches.

A final word, which should be self-evident but is sadly ignored too often: enterprise in collecting aquatic animals should be in direct proportion to your ability as a swimmer. The non-swimmer who falls into deep water while straining for some coveted specimen just beyond his reach is not only risking his own life, he is also endangering the life of the friend or chance bystander who has to try to save him.

Part Three

The Principles of Zoological Classification

The Phylum Arthropoda ("jointed-limbed ones"—crabs, insects, spiders, mites, etc.) is by far the largest in the Animal Kingdom, chiefly because of the immense number of species contributed by the Class Insecta. The animal phylum with the second largest number of species is the Mollusca. Many readers may be astonished at this. Nevertheless, with round about 112,000 species, the molluscs unquestionably do take second place, and of this number the Class Gastropoda (snails and slugs) provide about 85,000 and the Lamellibranchiata (mussels and other bivalves) about 25,000 species.

Some prospective mollusc enthusiasts may be shocked to learn of this enormous profusion of species and be on the point of becoming discouraged. They can be reassured: this book deals with the collection and identification of only 129 species of snails, 23 of slugs and 27 of mussels. This number should not be too difficult to master. The reasons for this considerable restriction in the numbers of our native British species are poorly known. In the first place, of course, the marine species are excluded from our present consideration. In the second, with molluscs, as with other groups, it is the tropics which produce the greatest profusion of species both on land and in the water, and we here are dealing with the fauna of a temperate country.

"Order is half of life", goes the saying. The branch of zoology to which this saying applies is systematics or taxonomy, the science which is concerned with the classification and naming of animals chiefly in regard to the characters of their external structure and internal anatomy. If animals resemble one another in all respects and recognise one another as belonging to the same kind, and if their males and females breed together to produce fertile offspring, then the systematist says that they form a group called a "species". Species distinguished from one another by relatively trifling but fixed hereditary characters are put together in a higher group called a "genus". As the distinctions become greater further genera are

40

erected and, according to the degree of their resemblance, are united to form a "family". Next, again, a group of families forms an "order". Bringing together the orders we form a "class"; thus, combining all the orders which exhibit snail-like characters, we arrive at the "snail-class" or Class Gastropoda. In the same way, we can set about classifying all the mussels, cockles, oysters, razorshells and so on into species, genera and families until finally we have four orders which we can bring together to form a "bivalve class", the Class Lamellibranchiata. Thus, while at the beginning of this book we glanced at the variety of molluscan form by looking at the classification at the highest level, now we have seen how this classification is built up from the bottom. It is true that it is hardly proper to compare a species (which is a group of individuals) with a soldier (who is only one), but if we accept the parallel for a moment we can see that, just as a species can be assigned to the correct hierarchy of groups in the classification, so it is possible to identify 1234567 Private Doe, J., and then say which platoon, company, battalion, regiment, division and army he belongs to.

This sequence of categories is illustrated by the following example, the Roman Snail (*Helix pomatia*). Its position in the zoological system is as follows:

Phylum: Mollusca (molluscs)
  Class: Gastropoda (snails and slugs)
    Order: Pulmonata (lunged-snails)
      Suborder: Stylommatophora (terrestrial lunged-snails)
        Superfamily: Helicacea
          Family: Helicidae
            Genus: *Helix*
              Species: *H. pomatia*

The systematist proceeds by arranging species in his system according to the degree of their external and internal structural resemblances. According to modern ideas of evolution the majority of such resemblances can be traced back to a common ancestor and so the system, if it has been correctly devised, should therefore indicate the degree of phylogenetic relationship, or "relationship by descent". For this reason such a system is also called a "Natural System", and is the ideal towards which the modern systematist aspires. Systems which, through ignorance or misjudgement, fall short of this ideal are called "Artificial". Thus, early naturalists, misled by their superficial resemblances, classified whales with fishes; later ones realised that whales are warm-blooded, breathe by lungs instead of gills, have a little hair, suckle their young and so on, and accordingly modified this artificial classification into a natural one which places whales among the mammals. In the same way certain little-known groups—such as the lamp-shells (Brachiopoda)—were once unnaturally classified with the molluscs.

The names of the various systematic groups (phyla, classes, orders, etc., down to species) are, as the above example of the Roman Snail shows, all derived from Latin roots or from Latinised Greek words. This custom began at a time when Latin was the universal language of scholars throughout the world. Today almost every scientist writes in his own mother tongue, yet we still follow the lead of the celebrated Swedish naturalist Carolus Linnaeus (or Carl von Linné: 1707–78) who first devised the system of "binominal nomenclature" whereby every plant and animal species is known to science by a combination of two Latin or Latinised words, of which the first indicates the genus and the second (*in combination with the first*) the species. It is customary also to add the name of the author who first described the species in a scientific publication and gave it this name. A bracket around the author's name indicates that he put the species into a genus other than the one now being used; thus *Helix nemoralis* Linnaeus becomes *Cepaea nemoralis* (Linnaeus) or *Cepaea nemoralis* (L.).

Thus naturalists the whole world over know precisely which animal is intended. But the Latin name can be an advantage even for two men who speak the same language, because the vernacular names of animals and plants vary very much from one district to another. The robins of Great Britain and North America are two entirely different species, for example, and a scientist studying alleged fishery-pests found that the names cormorant and shag are freely interchanged between two quite different birds every few miles along the Devonshire coast! Moreover, in many, indeed the great majority of cases, no common or vernacular names exist for plants and animals simply because ordinary folk have no need to mention unfamiliar species by name in their everyday life. Thus the scientific name becomes the sole available reference-point.

Systematists are often reviled by other biologists for their allegedly capricious and frequent changing of scientific names which often seems to destroy the advantages already claimed. Young specialists who pursue their interest beyond this book are very likely to join the opposition, for they will frequently find difficulty in reconciling the nomenclature used in the present book with that in any other they are likely to lay hands on. If we cannot remove this difficulty we can at least allay irritation by explaining some of the reasons which produce it.

Zoological nomenclature is, in fact, quite a complicated business, involving considerable experience, knowledge of procedure and knowledge of animals. Its principles are set out in a 200-page book of *Rules*, reconsidered every five years by the International Congresses of Zoology, and difficult points are decided by a permanent judicial body, the International Commission on Zoological Nomenclature. In general the guiding principles can be expressed as follows:

Every species of animal shall have a scientific name which must follow the binominal system introduced by Linnaeus. The same name shall not be applied to two different animals (no homonyms!), neither shall two names be applied to the same animal (no synonyms!). The starting-point for the whole system is the tenth edition of the *Systema Naturae* of Linnaeus, published in 1758, and thus any zoologist working in this field must have access to an encyclopaedic library of zoological literature from 1758 onwards. Many of the difficulties which arise do so because systematists publish without adequate reference to this vast literature or without adequate examination of the "type" specimens upon which other authors have based new species and which they have deposited for future reference in one or other of the world's great museums.

Generally speaking, names are usually changed for one of three reasons:

(1) Because a systematist finds that an earlier name for a species has been overlooked or that an earlier description has been misunderstood. Thus, provided they really apply to the same animal, the name *Alpha beta* Jones 1850 would be said to "have priority" over the names *Alpha gamma* Smith 1851 and *Alpha omega* Robinson 1852. Accordingly *Alpha beta* Jones would become the official name of the animal and *Alpha gamma* and *Alpha omega* would be rejected as junior synonyms which, at the same time, could not be used for any other animal in the genus *Alpha* either.

(2) Because a systematist finds that the same name has been used for two quite different animals. Thus, if it is discovered that Jones erected the genus *Alpha* for some molluscs in 1850, and that Brown had previously used *Alpha* for some grasshoppers in 1849, then the name of the mollusc genus would have to be changed. It might be found that *Lambda* Williams 1860, previously considered to be a synonym of *Alpha* Jones 1850, was available; if so, that would do. Otherwise, a new name would have to be devised and

then, provided that a search showed that the name had never been used before, we might see the publication of *Theta* Smith 1964!

(3) Because a systematist, revising a genus on a world-wide basis, decides that it contains two or more distinct groups of species and desires to signify the fact by giving them one or more new generic names. Thus Linnaeus' old genus *Helix* is now divided into *Helix* in a restricted sense, plus *Helicella, Cepaea, Arianta* and others.

It is a great nuisance, but there is method in the madness and one day we may hope to see an end to it! But we shall still need systematists!

The Classification of British Land and Freshwater Molluscs

At the beginning of this book it was explained that molluscs compose one of the great divisions or phyla of the Animal Kingdom, and that snails and mussels are members of two of the five classes into which this phylum is divided. Now, to provide a fuller picture, the text describes how our land and freshwater snails, slugs and freshwater mussels can be divided up into several groups and why they are classified in this way.

Class Gastropoda (Snails and Slugs)

Order 1. Prosobranchiata ("front-gilled ones"; Greek *pros*, forward and *branchia*, the gills of fishes).

Most prosobranchs possess a spirally coiled shell which can be closed by an operculum attached to the hinder end of the foot; the limpet-like forms are exceptional in that the shell retains little or no trace of the spiral structure and its mouth can be pulled tightly against the rock on which the animal sits, so rendering an operculum unnecessary. The eyes are situated at the bases of the single pair of cephalic tentacles. All prosobranchs agree in one especially important anatomical character, namely, that by a process of torsion or twisting of the visceral mass through 180° upon the foot, the respiratory chamber opens forwards and the gills lie in front of the heart. With the exception of the Valve Snails (Valvatidae), which are hermaphrodite, all our native species have the sexes separate. Again, with very few exceptions, all prosobranchs are aquatic, in freshwater or in the sea.

Prosobranchs are further classified according to the appearance and structure of their gills, thus:

Suborder a. Aspidobranchiata ("shield-gilled ones": Greek *aspis, aspidos*, a shield).

Prosobranchs with one or two gills, each composed of two rows of gill-leaflets. Heart with two auricles (hence also the name Diotocardia for the suborder). Apart from numerous marine species we have one freshwater family, the Neritidae, containing one species, the Freshwater Nerite (*Theodoxus fluviatilis*).

Suborder b. Pectinibranchiata ("comb-gilled ones"; Latin *pecten, pectinis*, a comb).

Prosobranchs with one gill, composed of a single pair of gill-leaflets. Heart with one auricle (hence also the name Monotocardia for the suborder). Apart from numerous marine species we have representatives of six families. Four of these are freshwater, including the River Snails (Viviparidae), the Valve Snails (Valvatidae) and the Snouted Water-snails (Hydrobiidae). Two are terrestrial: the Point Snails (Acmidae), which retain the gill, and the Round-mouthed Snails or Land Winkles (Pomatiasidae) in which the gill is replaced by a capillary network which forms a lung on the roof of the respiratory chamber so that the animals, although still confined to damp places, can breathe atmospheric air.

Order 2. Opisthobranchiata ("rear-gilled ones": Greek *opisthen*, rear).

Opisthobranchs are descended from prosobranchs which have undergone a process of de-torsion so that the gill has returned to the rear. Both the single gill and the shell tend to be much reduced or absent. Opisthobranchs include sea-hares, sea-slugs and pteropods or sea-butterflies, all marine forms which do not concern us further in this book.

Order 3. Pulmonata ("lunged-ones": New Latin *pulmonatus*, having lungs).

Pulmonates are gastropods in which the body shows the effects of torsion but in which, unlike the prosobranchs, the nervous system has attained a secondary symmetry through the concentration of the nerve ganglia to form a sort of necklace around the oesophagus. The shell is very variable: usually it is well developed and spirally coiled, but in some cases it is helmet- or bonnet-shaped with little or no trace of coiling, or again—as in the slugs—reduced to a small calcareous rudiment underneath the mantle-shield. There is no operculum to close the mouth of the shell. There are no gills; respiration is usually by means of a capillary network forming a "lung" on the roof of the respiratory chamber. The great majority of species—marine, freshwater and terrestrial—breathe air, but a few deepwater ones have the mantle-cavity permanently filled with water. All pulmonates are hermaphrodite and the young develop directly from the egg without any intervening larval stage.

There are two suborders:

Suborder a. Stylommatophora ("stalked-eyed ones": Greek *stylos*, a style or pillar; *omma, ommatos*, an eye; *phoros*, a bearing).

Terrestrial pulmonates with two pairs of retractile cephalic tentacles which can be turned outside-in into the body like the fingers of a glove. The eyes are situated at the tips of the hinder pair (Figure 18a).

Figure 18. Heads of Pulmonate Snails: a Stylommatophoran type; b Basommatophoran type. E Eyes. (After Forcart.)

We have fifteen families, including the Helicidae, the largest and best-known group of land-snails and also three families of slugs (Testacellidae, Arionidae and Limacidae).

Suborder b. Basommatophora ("basal-eyed ones": Greek *basis*, base, bottom).

Aquatic pulmonates, with only one pair of cephalic tentacles which are at most contractile and not retractile. The eyes are situated at the bases of the tentacles (Figure 18b).

Apart from a few species on the seashore we have six freshwater families, of which the Pond Snails (Lymnaeidae), Ramshorn Snails (Planorbidae) and Freshwater Limpets (Ancylidae and Acroloxidae) are the best known.

Class Lamellibranchiata (Mussels and Other Bivalves)

There are four orders of lamellibranchs, classified according to the structure of their gills. Since all our freshwater mussels and their relatives belong to one of these orders, the Eulamellibranchiata, the remaining three do not really concern us. However, a brief synopsis of the full classification of the class is given so as to place the freshwater species in their proper context.

Order 1. Protobranchiata ("primitive-gilled ones": Greek *protos*, first, primary; *branchia*, the gills of fishes).

Primitive lamellibranchs in which there are two rows of gill-filaments suspended from the roof of each gill-chamber, rather like those American-style walk-through door-curtains. The ends of the gill-filaments hang freely and are not reflected (turned-up) or

46

joined to one another. We have a few small species, all marine, of which the best known are the Nut-shells (*Nucula*).

Order 2. Filibranchiata ("thread-gilled ones": Latin *filum*, a thread).

Lamellibranchs in which the gill-filaments are reflected and adjacent ones are united by tufts of cilia. (Commencing with the walk-through curtain analogy described above, imagine the lower end of each strip of the pair of curtains lifted up and attached to the top of the doorway, so that the curtain is now four strips thick instead of two. Then imagine little tufts of bristles at intervals along each strip, catching against the bristles on adjacent strips, and you have the exact picture!)

We have many species, all marine, including the Mussel (*Mytilus edulis*) and the Scallops (*Pecten*).

Order 3. Eulamellibranchiata ("perfect leaf-gilled ones": Greek *eu*, good, true; other roots as for Lamellibranchiata, *see* p. 12).

Lamellibranchs in which the gill-filaments are reflected as in the Filibranchs (*above*), but with permanent junctions, which contain blood-vessels, between adjacent filaments (Figure 10). There are nearly always two adductor muscles between the valves of the shell. The inhalant and exhalant respiratory openings are often produced to form tubular siphons. The families are recognised largely on the structure of the teeth in the hinge and the form of the scars left by the adductor muscles.

As well as numerous marine forms, such as the Oyster (*Ostrea*) and Cockle (*Cardium*), there are four families which contain all our freshwater mussels.

Order 4. Septibranchiata ("partition-gilled ones": Latin *septum*, a partition).

Lamellibranchs in which the gills have ceased to function as such and form two horizontal, longitudinal, muscular partitions along the gill-chambers. Only a few, rare, deepwater marine species.

Part Four

How to Identify Snails and Slugs

To perfect the skill of identification, you must be prepared to weigh the descriptions on the following pages very carefully against one another and compare them point by point with your snail-shells. Likewise, the details of specimens must be minutely compared with those of the corresponding illustrations.

Prior to this, however, some further explanation is necessary. We must first of all examine a snail-shell from tip to mouth, identify all the most important parts of its structure, and learn the precise meanings of the terms employed in the scientific descriptions of the various species.

From the tip, or apex, of the shell the several coils, or whorls, follow one another in a close spiral and increase in breadth towards the mouth or aperture. The last and largest whorl is called the body-whorl; the preceding series together constitute the spire. If the whorls are coiled like a corkscrew, the resulting shell is spire-shaped; if, on the other hand, they all lie in one plane, then the shell is disc-shaped. Between and apart from these two extremes there are many intermediate and additional forms, variously described as spindle-, needle, cone-, or dish-shaped, and so on. If the whorls are closely approximated in the centre of the spiral, then a more or less massive axis or columella is formed (Figure 6), while if they are coiled rather more loosely the columella becomes hollow and acquires an umbilicus. The umbilical opening, situated opposite the apex, may be very wide (basin-shaped in perspective), wide, narrow (perforate) or very narrow (pierced) or, again, it may be overlain by the columellar lip (*see below*) to the extent that it is partly covered, reduced to a chink (cleft), or covered.

The line along which adjacent whorls meet is called the suture and is marked by a more or less conspicuous groove. There may also be fine spiral grooves, or striae, on the whorls themselves, or a prominent spiral ridge forming a keel. Again, there may be transverse ridges or ribs across the whorls, lying parallel to the main axis of the shell.

The opening of the shell, through which the animal emerges, is called the mouth or aperture. The edge of the mouth, or peristome, is the growing region of the shell and may be regarded as being composed of an outer lip, lying away from the shell axis, and an inner or columellar lip lying close to the shell axis. The peristome and its lips may be ∪-shaped, the open part of the ∪ being bounded by the surface of the last whorl but one; this boundary is known as the parietal region, and in some cases the peristome grows narrowly across to form a parietal lip. In others, the two limbs of the ∪ are more or less widely separated, and the parietal lip is represented by no more than a glaze over the surface of the parietal region. The peristome exhibits a great many modifications in different species; it may be simple, straight and sharp, or incurved (inflected), curved outwards (dilated or expanded), or turned back on itself (reflected), and it may be thickened and strengthened to form a glazed ridge, the lip. Finally various tooth-like or enamel-ridge formations may be developed from different parts of the walls of the mouth with a consequent interruption or narrowing of the opening.

Since these several mouth-reinforcements—lips, ribs, teeth, ridges, etc.—are only distinctly formed in the shells of full-grown animals, they provide useful criteria for judging the maturity of many species. Even in cases where the peristome remains simple, straight and sharp in the adult, there may be another means of answering the question "juvenile or full-grown?" If the edge of the mouth is still soft and flexible while the shell is otherwise quite firm, then the animal is pretty certainly not full-grown. If such tests fail, then you can only settle the matter by measuring the size of the shell and comparing it with many other shells of the same and related species.

Often the direction of the spiral coil of the shell is also a significant character in the identification of species. In order to determine this, hold the shell so that the apex is upwards and the mouth faces you. Then, if the mouth lies to the right of the vertical axis of the shell, we say that it is coiled to the right, or dextral; if it lies to the left, then it is coiled to the left and is called sinistral. It may be noted in passing that the direction of coiling is hereditarily determined and, just as in man the heart normally lies towards the left side, so in both cases there may be exceptional individuals which display the contrary condition (*see* p. 132, No. 152).

To make accurate identifications, the collector must further master two special techniques: firstly, that of measuring the height and breadth of a shell with a sliding caliper and, secondly, that of counting the whorls.

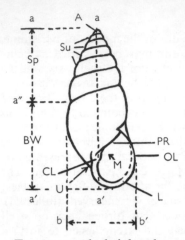

Figure 19. Diagram of a snail-shell, showing the various parts and points between which measurements are taken. A Apex, BW Body Whorl, CL Columellar Lip, L Lip, M Mouth or Aperture, OL Outer Lip, PR Parietal Region, Sp Spire, Su Suture, U Umbilicus. a–a′ Height and Axis of shell. b–b′ Breadth of Shell. a–a″ Height of Spire, a′–a″ Height of Body Whorl. 1–7 Whorls of Shell; here 1–6 form the Spire and 7 is the Body Whorl.

To measure the height, always hold the shell upright, mounted on the inner axis which runs through the columella (a–a′ in Figure 19), and position the two arms of the caliper exactly perpendicular to this axis (Figure 20a). In measuring the breadth, hold the shell with the axis horizontal and then grip the greatest width with the caliper, whose arms now lie parallel to the axis of the shell (Figure 20b). These and other scientific measurements employ the metric system which has the advantages that it combines a fine unit of measurement (1 mm. equals approximately $\frac{1}{25}$ in.) with a decimal system which obviates vulgar fractions and is capable of infinite subdivision for still finer and more accurate measurements. We can compare 7 and 8 mm. at a glance; comparing $\frac{3}{10}$ and $\frac{5}{16}$ in. requires some cogitation, while $3\frac{1}{2}/10$ and $5\frac{1}{2}/16$ in. might improve our mathematics but not our tempers!

For counting the whorls, too, an exact orientation is required. Commence counting at the inmost point of the small semi-circle (0 in Figure 21) which always stands out quite clearly on the apex,

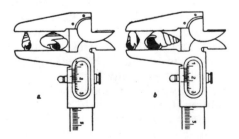

Figure 20. Measuring the height (a) and breadth (b) of a snail-shell.

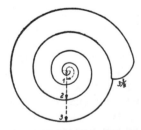

Figure 21. Method of counting the whorls. For explanation see text.

50

especially when the shell is examined through a hand-lens. Then follow the broken radial line in the direction indicated by the arrows until you arrive at point 1, which counts as the end of the first whorl. From there, continue counting each further whorl across the shell until you arrive at the periphery (point 3 in the drawing) and finally consider what fraction of the final coil has not been included in the count. In Figure 21 there are three full whorls plus three-quarters of a turn of the final whorl, so the count becomes $3\frac{3}{4}$. After a little practice, you should obtain measurements and counts sufficiently precise to provide valuable data towards species-identification.

Having digested this information, you are now sufficiently equipped to undertake your first attempts at identifying specimens with the aid of the illustrations and descriptions on the following pages. In order to avoid having to skim through all these pages from the beginning, or having to dip into them at random, use the key on page 53 which, in most cases, will narrow the field of possibilities to the members of one family and sometimes even to the correct genus or species. Several kinds of keys are used in taxonomy, and more than one type will be encountered in this book, but all of them work on the principle of confronting the user with a pair of alternatives (tall or low, smooth or hairy, red or brown, etc.), each chosen alternative being followed by an indication leading to another pair until finally, if we have decided each choice correctly, we arrive at the true identification of our specimen.

Notes on the Species Descriptions

Each species description should be read in conjunction with the preceding general account of the family (and with the key if there is one) which contains general supplementary information.

Species descriptions are given in a standardised form so as to facilitate comparison. Superficial characters such as glossiness, hairiness and colour are deliberately given last so as to force a careful preliminary study of form and structure. Major variations are described but the many minor ones are beyond the scope of a book of this length and are left to the more advanced works listed in the Bibliography.

Shells may be assumed to be dextral (right-wound) in the absence of any definite statement to the contrary.

No good naturalist is ever without a pocket magnifying-glass. Nevertheless we have included an occasional reminder that a structure or feature cannot be seen by the naked eye. "(Lens)" indicates that a magnification of 6–8 diameters is required; "(lens!)" a magnification of 12–16 diameters.

In the abbreviated formulae, H = Height, B = Breadth, W = Number of Whorls; height and breadth are expressed in millimetres.

Under "Distribution" brief indications are given of the distribution of each species within the British Isles and elsewhere. For more detailed information the Conchological Society's *Census* should be consulted. The usual abbreviations are used for the points of the compass, otherwise C = Central.

Zoologists recognise certain major zoogeographical regions of the world characterised by their possession of distinctive faunas or groups of animal species. The names of such regions may be applied as adjectives descriptive of the distribution of a species, genus, family or higher group, and here we meet three of them:

> Nearctic = North America
> Palaearctic = Europe plus Asia north of the Himalayas
> Holarctic = Nearctic and Palaearctic together

Most British species fall into one or other of these categories. More restricted distributions within Europe are sometimes exactly specified by countries or limits, sometimes as follows:

> Mediterranean = distributed through the regions adjacent to and bordering on the Mediterranean Sea
> Lusitanian = distributed through those European districts influenced by warm Atlantic currents, viz. S.W. Ireland, Cornwall, Brittany, the Channel Islands and N.W. Spain
> Arctic-alpine = distributed through cold regions, such as the countries on the Arctic Circle, the high Alps, Pyrenees and sometimes Snowdonia, the Pennines and the Scottish mountains
> Endemic = confined to one small area and found nowhere else in the world
> Relict = a species which once ranged over a wide area which presented suitable conditions and is now restricted to a few small areas in which those conditions still prevail, e.g. patches of old forest, cold lakes, high mountains, etc.

The lines by the illustrations indicate the actual height or breadth of the species; divided lines indicate the range of variation in height or breadth (from . . . to . . .).

The general key below commences with a choice between (I) water snails and (II) land snails. Having decided this, you must then examine the animal to see whether it comes into categories (A), (B) or (C), being Prosobranchiata, Basommatophora or Stylommatophora respectively. Proceeding further, there are in each section Groups 1, 2, 3, etc., all of which are alternative choices, and sometimes again within each group further choices a, b, c, etc., which lead to the appropriate families. The more striking characters are given earlier in the key so that you can dispose of as many easy identifications as possible before coming to the difficult residues. II (C), 6 and 7 *are* difficult—but that is the way Nature makes the creatures and it is no use complaining!

Key to the Families of British Land and Freshwater Snails

I. WATER SNAILS

A. Animal with an operculum, one pair of tentacles, eyes at the bases of the tentacles.

1. Shell shaped like an obliquely sliced egg   Neritidae, p. 56

2. Shell disc-shaped; animal with a feathery external gill (*Valvata cristata*)   Valvatidae, p. 58

3. Shell conical-globose to spire-shaped:
   a. Very large (H to 40 mm.), thick, with a pointed apex and spiral bands   Viviparidae, p 56
   b. Animal with a feathery external gill; shell small, with a squat spire; H to 5 mm.   Valvatidae, p. 58
   c. No feathery external gill; tentacles thread-like; shell conical-globose to cylindrical or spire-shaped; H to 15 mm., mostly much less   Hydrobiidae, p. 61
   d. As (c), but with short, stubby tentacles   Assimineidae, p. 64

B. Animal without an operculum, with two pairs of tentacles and eyes at the bases of the posterior pair

1. Shell limpet-like
   a. Apex pointed, hooked to right   Ancylidae, p. 76
   b. Apex blunt, inclined to left   Acroloxidae, p. 76

2. Shell disc-like, coiled in a plane spiral   Planorbidae, p. 70

3. Shell globose with a long or short spire
   a. Shell dextral   Lymnaeidae, p. 66
   b. Shell sinistral   Physidae, p. 66

C. Animal without an operculum, with two pairs of tentacles (the anterior pair reduced) and eyes at the tips of the posterior pair

Shell dextral, horny, globose with a long or short spire; animal lives on and among marsh plants, seldom in the water   Succineidae, p. 78

II. LAND SNAILS

A. Animal with an operculum, one pair of tentacles, eyes at the bases of the tentacles

    1. Shell slender, cylindrical, with an elliptical mouth   Acmidae, p. 60

    2. Shell globose, with a conical spire and a round mouth   Pomatiasidae, p. 60

    3. Shell as (2), but with a triangular mouth; lives near high-water spring tides   Assimineidae, p. 64

B. Animal without an operculum, with two pairs of tentacles and eyes at the bases of the posterior pair

    Shell dextral, spindle-shaped, with teeth inside the mouth   Ellobiidae, p. 64

C. Animal without an operculum, with two pairs of tentacles (the anterior pair sometimes reduced) and eyes at the tips of the posterior pair

    1. Animal naked, or with only a tiny posterior shell   Slugs, p. 97

    2. Shell with coloured bands, a pattern of markings or uniformly brightly coloured   Helicidae, p. 116

    3. Shell prickly, bristly or hairy

        a. Shell conical, H to 2 mm., with transverse ribs each bearing a sharp spine (*Acanthinula aculeata*)   Valloniidae, p. 88

        b. Shell globose or flattened, covered with fine hairs or bristles (*Hygromia* and *Monacha* spp.)   Helicidae, p. 116

    4. Shell with teeth inside the mouth

        a. Shell sinistral, club-shaped, H to 16 mm.   Clausiliidae, p. 92

        b. Shell sinistral or dextral, dumpy spire-shaped to cylindrical, H to 8 mm. but mostly smaller   Vertiginidae, p. 82

        c. Shell dextral, spindle-shaped, glossy and translucent, H: 6·5 mm. (*Azeca*)   Cochlicopidae, p. 80

        d. Shell dextral, thick disc-shaped, with two broad, low teeth (*Helicodonta obvoluta*)   Helicidae, p. 116

    5. Shell elongate to very elongate, without teeth inside the mouth

        a. Shell sinistral, club-shaped, H: 8–9 mm., B: 2·0–2·5 mm. (*Balea perversa*)   Clausiliidae, p. 92

        b. Shell dextral, cylindrical or subcylindrical, with a blunt or rounded apex, horn-brown, H to 2·6 mm., B to 1·4 mm. (*Truncatella, Columella*)   Vertiginidae, p. 82

        c. Shell dextral, spire-shaped, with a truncated apex and truncated columella, milky, H: 5 mm., B: 1·3 mm.; animal burrows deep in the soil   Ferussaciidae, p. 96

        d. Shell dextral, elongate ovoid to cylindrical with a rib inside the peristome, very smooth, glossy, transparent, brownish to violet, H to 7 mm.   Cochlicopidae, p. 80

e. Shell dextral, oval with a blunt conical spire, thickened peristome, brownish, H to 18 mm., B to 6 mm. — Enidae, p. 90

f. Shell dextral, oval with a conical spire and a thin, sharp peristome, horny, transparent, amber-coloured, H to 23 mm., B to 13 mm.; animal too large for shell, lives in marshy places — Succineidae, p. 78

g. Shell dextral, spire-shaped, white with brown streaks, H: 15–26 mm., B: 5·5–7 mm. (*Cochlicella*) — Helicidae, p. 116

6. Shell depressed-globose to disc-shaped (i.e., breadth much greater than height)

  a. Shell flattened and elliptical, with an expanded and thickened peristome, H: 1·2 mm., B: 2·3 mm. — Valloniidae, p. 88

  b. Shell flattened and round, with a thin, simple, sharp peristome and nearly circular mouth, H to 3 mm., B to 7·5 mm. — Endodontidae, p. 114

  c. Shell flattened and round, with a thin, simple, sharp peristome and an elliptical mouth, sometimes with a lip, H to 7 mm., B to 14 mm. A pedal groove around the edge of the foot — Zonitidae, p. 109

  d. As (c), but shell in living animal partly covered by the mantle, H to 3·4 mm., B to 6 mm. — Vitrinidae, p. 114

  e. Shell as large or larger than the above, usually more opaque, with various unusual features such as a peripheral keel, hairs or bristles, chalky or pigmented surfaces, etc. No pedal groove around the edge of the foot — Helicidae, p. 116

7. Shell more or less globose (i.e., height and breadth not differing greatly one way or the other)

  a. Shell shaped like a typical *Helix* but with more whorls than a *Helix* would have at this small size (H: 1·8 mm., B: 3.0 mm.; W: 4–4½) and a thicker shell; dark red-brown — Pyramidulidae, p. 80

  b. More globose species of families 6a, c–e above — Valloniidae, p. 88 / Zonitidae, p. 109 / Vitrinidae, p. 114 / Helicidae, p. 116

Class Gastropoda

Order Prosobranchiata (=Streptoneura)

SUBORDER ASPIDOBRANCHIATA (=DIOTOCARDIA)

SUPERFAMILY NERITACEA

Family Neritidae (Nerites)

Family with the characters of the single British species.

1. Freshwater Nerite: *Theodoxus fluviatilis* (L.). Shell dextral, small, obliquely ovoid, very thick-walled, with scarcely elevated spire; last whorl greatly enlarged; mouth semicircular, closable by corresponding spirally grooved limy operculum; edge of lip sharp; no umbilicus; colour whitish, dirty yellow or pale grey with network of dark markings. H: 6 mm., B: 11 mm., W: 2½. Lays 50–60 eggs in a capsule attached to another shell; owing to cannibalism among embryos, only one young snail survives. Prefers hard water: gravel or pebble bottoms of swift rivers and streams and wave-wash zones of lakes. Distribution: Somerset to Westmorland, Glamorgan, Orkney, Ireland; elsewhere throughout Europe, N. Africa.

SUBORDER PECTINIBRANCHIATA (=MONOTOCARDIA)

SUPERFAMILY CYCLOPHORACEA

Family Viviparidae (River Snails)

Family with the characters of the two British species.

2. River Snail: *Viviparus viviparus* (L.). Shell dextral, very large, not very glossy, thick, conical-rounded with blunt apex; spire arched with deep suture; mouth obliquely oval, closable by corresponding concentrically grooved horny operculum; edge of lip blunt and almost continuous; umbilicus reduced to chink by reflected columellar lip; colour green-brown with three dark bands (sometimes absent), often with different-coloured extraneous growths. H: 30–40 mm., B: 24–30 mm., W: 6–6½. Live-bearer; young shells hairy and spinous. Prefers hard water; slow-flowing, weedy rivers and canals. Distribution: England and Wales north to Yorkshire, but not extreme south and west; elsewhere throughout Europe into Asia.

3. Lister's River Snail: *Viviparus fasciatus* (Müller). Differs from *V. viviparus* in having thinner, glossy shell with sharper apex, deeper suture giving very "stepped" appearance to swollen whorls, rounder mouth and operculum and distinct and deep umbilicus. H: 32–35 mm., B: 22–30 mm., W: 6–7. Habitat, as above, but more local. Distribution: E. England north to Yorkshire, absent from S.W., S.E. and W. Midlands; elsewhere throughout Europe into Asia.

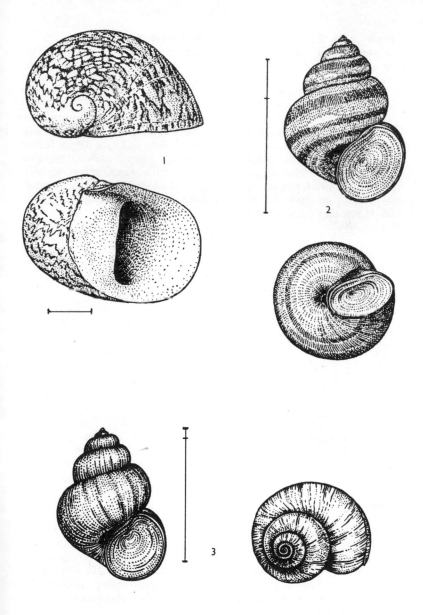

1

2

3

Family *Valvatidae* (*Valve Snails*)

Family with the characters of the three British species.

4. Common Valve Snail: *Valvata* (*Cincinna*) *piscinalis* (Müller). Shell dextral, small, globular, with a blunt conical spire almost as tall as the diameter of the mouth; first two whorls depressed, rest well arched, last large; fine, close rib-striations (lens); suture deep; mouth almost circular with continuous slightly dilated lip and spirally grooved operculum; umbilicus narrow, somewhat covered; colour shining greenish or yellowish. H: 5 mm., B: 5 mm., W: 4–4½. Mobile feathery gill and simple branchial process project from mantle cavity, snout is long and foot deeply forked at front (Figure 22). Hermaphrodite (unusual among prosobranchs), with permanently protruded penis. Tolerates soft water, prefers running water, but is found in all kinds of rivers, streams and lakes. Distribution: throughout British Isles, sporadic in N. Scotland; elsewhere through Europe to Asia Minor and on to Tibet.

Figure 22. Common Valve Snail (living animal, ×3). G Gill (branchial filament opposite), M Mouth (at end of long snout), O Operculum. Note also characteristic deep cleft at front of foot and permanently protruded penis behind tentacles.

5. Large-mouthed Valve Snail: *Valvata* (*C.*) *macrostoma* Mörch. Differs from above in smaller size, broad umbilicus, depressed spire, more dilated body-whorl, larger mouth, darker colour and glossy surface. H: 2 mm., B: 3·5–4 mm., W: 3½. Local in marshes and drains with rich fauna. Distribution: Hampshire, Sussex and East Anglia; elsewhere Central and N. Europe.

6. Flat Valve Snail: *Valvata* (*V.*) *cristata* Müller. A very atypical *Valvata*, like a small *Planorbis*, but dextral and easily distinguished by the feathery gill, forked foot and operculum. Shell disc-like, thin and glossy; suture deep; mouth round; umbilicus wide. H: 1·25 mm., B: 2–4 mm., W: 5. Lives in slow-flowing and stagnant waters. Distribution: British Isles, except Cornwall and parts of Scottish Highlands; elsewhere through N. Europe and Asia.

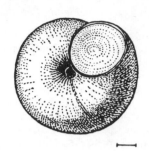

4

5

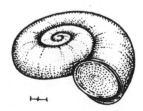

6

Family *Pomatiasidae* (*Land Winkles*)

Family with the characters of the single British species.
7. Round-mouthed Snail: *Pomatias elegans* (Müller). Shell dextral, ovoid with blunt conical spire; first two whorls form smooth, bluntly pointed apex, remainder are criss-crossed with spiral ridges and transverse striations; mouth almost circular; lip continuous, blunt, not dilated; umbilicus usually only cleft; colour of apex pale to violet-brown, otherwise grey to yellowish-white or flesh-coloured; a darker triple band is often broken up into spots, and bands 1 and 3 are sometimes missing. H: 10–17 mm., B: 8–13 mm., W: $4\frac{3}{4}$–5. Gill lost, replaced by vascular air-breathing lung. Front end of foot forked; two parts move alternately! Animal burrows in loose soil and moist leaf-mould in woods and hedges on limestone and chalk soils. Distribution: mainly S. and E. England, parts of N. England and N. and S. Wales; elsewhere W. and S. Europe, Asia Minor, N. Africa.

Family *Acmidae* (*Point Snails*)

Family with the characters of the single British species.
8. Point Snail: *Acme fusca* (Montagu). Shell dextral, minute ("point"), long, cylindrical; apex blunt; whorls increase very gradually and have transverse striations (lens!); mouth oval with horny operculum; umbilicus minute; colour shining yellowish or brownish. H: 2–2·5 mm., B: 0·5–0·75 mm., W: 6–7. Animal white with brown spots. Like *Pomatias*, a winkle "come ashore"; lung replaces gill. Almost aquatic among very damp moss and dead leaves in old woods, often on chalk or limestone, but in more acid conditions than *Pomatias*. Distribution: sporadic through England, Wales, N.W. Scotland and Ireland; elsewhere W. Europe.

7

8

Family *Hydrobiidae* (*Snouted Water-snails*)

Small water-snails with ovoid, spire-shaped or nearly cylindrical dextral shells, easily distinguished from the Limnaeidae and Succineidae by their possession of an operculum (often screened by a lobe of the foot), broader foot, thread-like tentacles and long snouts. A key to the 8 British species follows; if some of the distinctions appear fine it must be remembered that there is a high degree of ecological segregation between species and that the animals usually occur in such large numbers that it is easy to characterise a population.

KEY TO THE BRITISH HYDROBIIDAE

1. Operculum limy, concentrically grooved; freshwater animals (*Bithynia*).... 2
   Operculum horny, spirally grooved; mainly brackish-water animals......... 3

2. Shell to 15 mm. high; suture shallow; mouth oval.......... *Bithynia tentaculata*
   Shell to 6½ mm. high; suture deep; mouth round.................... *B. leachi*

3. Shell swollen, breadth more than half height........................... 4
   Shell-breadth half height or less...................................... 5

4. Shell to 3 mm. high, whorls 4; sulphur spots above eyes...... *Bythinella scholtzi*
   Shell to 4 mm. high, whorls 5–6.................... *Pseudamnicola confusa*

5. Shell nearly cylindrical in adult (apex shed).......... *Truncatella subcylindrica*
   Shell spire-like in adult (apex retained)............................... 6

6. Body-whorl more than half shell-height............... *Potamopyrgus jenkinsi*
   Body-whorl half shell-height or less (*Hydrobia*)........................ 7

7. Whorls flattened... *Hydrobia ulvae*
   Whorls swollen... *H. ventrosa*

9. Common Bithynia: *Bithynia tentaculata* (**L.**). The largest British Hydrobiid. Shell conical, with a pointed spire and rounded base; mouth oval, lip continuous; suture shallow; hardly any umbilicus; colour yellowish. H: 15 mm., B: 6 mm., W: 5–6. Animal collects small food with long, cleft snout. Female plants egg-capsules (1 egg each) in rows like strips of honeycomb. Prefers hard water, in quiet rivers and lakes. Distribution: Great Britain (except W. Wales) north to Stirling, and Ireland; elsewhere Europe, W. Siberia, N.W. Africa and introduced in N. America.

10. Leach's Bithynia: *Bithynia leachi* (**Sheppard**). Shell half size of *B. tentaculata*, thinner, with a sharp apex to the short spire, a deeper suture and swollen whorls; mouth round; umbilicus small but distinct. H: 6·5 mm., B: 4·5 mm., W: 4–5. More local than above; prefers hard, slow, thickly weeded waters. Distribution: England (except S.W.), local in Wales, S. Central Ireland; elsewhere Europe and N. Asia.

11. Laver Spire Snail: *Hydrobia ulvae* (Pennant). Shell conical, thick, smooth, with elongate blunt spire; suture shallow, whorls flattened, body-whorl half height; mouth nearly round, columellar lip reflected; no umbilicus; colour black through yellow to white. H: 10 mm., B: 5 mm., W: 4–6. Animal has dark ring towards tip of each tentacle and dark line across middle of snout; snout broadens towards divided tip. Egg-capsules (3–25 eggs) attached to another snail. Vast numbers on green seaweeds (Laver = *Ulva*) in estuaries or on surface of mud-flats. Local races differ, but species in general tolerates more brackish water than *H. ventrosa* (below). Distribution: all coasts England, Wales, Ireland, sporadic around Scotland; elsewhere N.W. Europe.

12. Spire Snail: *Hydrobia ventrosa* (Montagu). Shell smaller than *H. ulvae*, thin, glossy; suture deep, whorls well-rounded; mouth ear-shaped; colour pale brown (animal shows through black). H: 8·4 mm., B: 3·2 mm., W: 6. Animal lacks markings noted above; sides of snout parallel. Lower salinity-tolerance than *H. ulvae*; prefers brackish lagoons not directly connected with sea. Distribution: south and east coasts England, Bristol Channel, Outer Hebrides, Anglesey, very local in Ireland; elsewhere W. Europe to Baltic.

13. Jenkins' Spire Snail: *Potamopyrgus jenkinsi* (E. A. Smith). Shell pointed, spire-like, sometimes with spiral keel or row of spines; mouth pear-shaped, lip raised; umbilicus cleft; colour yellow crusted with black. H: 5·5 mm., B: 3 mm., W: 5–6. Animal darkly pigmented; end of snout broadened into two semicircular lobes. Viviparous and parthenogenetic (only one male ever found). Appeared from nowhere in mid-19th century as brackish-water species and started moving into fresh water about 1893; story repeated in Europe. Vast numbers on stones, weed or mud in brackish or freshwater where there is some current. Distribution: most of British Isles, except W. and N. Scotland and Central Ireland; elsewhere N. Europe to Baltic and Black Sea.

14. Taylor's Spire Snail: *Bythinella scholzi* (A. Schmidt). Our smallest Hydrobiid. Shell elongate egg-shaped with a flattened apex; suture deep, whorls swollen, increasing rapidly in size; mouth broadly oval, outer lip simple, columellar lip thickened and slightly reflexed; colour greenish-brown with black deposit. H: 2·5 mm., B: 1·3 mm., W: 4. Animal has sulphur spots above eyes; thread-like tentacles can contract to small spheres (probably more diagnostic than shell-characters). Egg-capsule contains single large egg. Introduced from America in 1900; fossils here previously. Feeds on decaying reed meadow grass (*Glyceria*). Distribution: canals in Cheshire and Lancashire, dock at Grangemouth, Stirlingshire; elsewhere N. and Central Europe to Finland and S.W. Russia.

15. Swollen Spire Snail: *Pseudamnicola confusa* (Frauenfeld). Shell thin, swollen, whorls swollen, but flattened above; suture deep; body-whorl very large; mouth pear-shaped; umbilicus small; colour pale brown. H: 4 mm., B: 3 mm., W: 5–6. Biology little known; lives in brackish to nearly fresh water. Distribution: local: Sussex, Suffolk, Norfolk, Lincolnshire in England; Shannon, Suir, Barrow and Nore estuaries in Ireland; elsewhere S.W. Europe, N. Africa, Madeira.

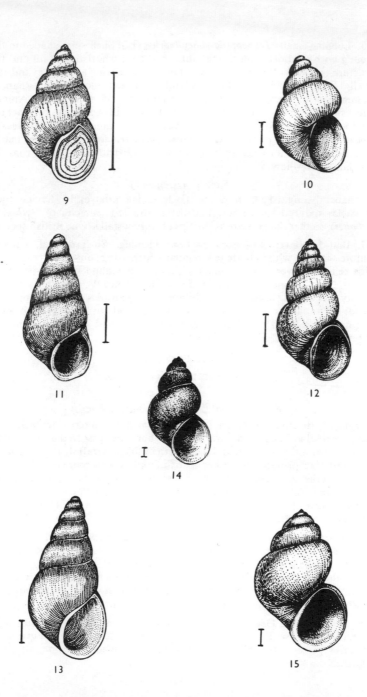

16. Looping Snail: *Truncatella subcylindrica* (L.). Shell spire-shaped in the young with 6 whorls, but in the adult the first 3 whorls break off and the fracture is sealed off previously by a limy plate, leaving a nearly cylindrical shell. Suture shallow; whorls slightly convex; mouth drop-shaped; columellar lip slightly reflected. H: 4 mm., B: 1·5 mm., W: 3. Animal moves like a leech or a looper (Geometrid) caterpillar, alternately attaching its foot and the end of its snout. Lives on mud among seablite (*Suaeda maritima*) and sea purslane (*Halimione portulacoides*) at high-tide mark; retains gill and can breathe in air or water. Distribution: south coast of England; elsewhere W. Europe.

Family Assimineidae

Snails distinguished from the Hydrobiidae (above) by having their tentacles reduced to stumps (like the contracted tentacles of *Bythinella scholtzi*), so that the eyes are at the tips of stubby stalks. One British species.

17. Dun Sentinel: *Assiminea grayana* Fleming. Shell dextral, conical, suture shallow, whorls flattened, regularly increasing; outer and columellar lips reflected over now triangular mouth; operculum horny with spiral grooves; colour glossy brown. H: 5 mm., B: 3 mm., W: 6. No gill; mantle-cavity acts as lung. Snout broad, bilobed. Egg-capsules (1 egg) dropped on mud. Abundant among grasses and sedges and on mud at high-water spring-tide level. Distribution: east coast England, Kent to Humber; elsewhere Belgium, Holland, Denmark.

ORDER PULMONATA

SUBORDER BASOMMATOPHORA

SUPERFAMILY ELLOBIACEA

Family Ellobiidae (Hollow-shelled Snails)

Small, primitive lunged-snails with rudimentary anterior tentacles and no pallial lobe. The internal walls of the whorls are dissolved to make more room as the animal grows, and the mouth of the (dextral) shell is obstructed by tooth-like projections. Other British families with more or less similar shell-mouths are readily distinguished by their stalked eyes; here, of course, the eyes are at the bases of the posterior tentacles.

Carychium (3 mouth-teeth) is terrestrial; *Leucophytia* (2 teeth) and *Phytia* (5–6 teeth) are both estuarine.

18. Short-toothed Herald Snail: *Carychium minimum* Müller. Shell thin, spindle-shaped, with a blunt apex; lip thickened and reflected; mouth oval with a thickened, reflected peristome and 3 short teeth arising, 1 each, from the outer, columellar and parietal lips; colour white. H: 2 mm., B: 1 mm., W: 5. Common in damp leaf-mould, rotten wood, grass-roots, etc. Distribution: throughout the British Isles; elsewhere Europe.

19. Long-toothed Herald Snail: *Carychium tridentatum* (Risso). Similar to the above, but with more pronounced teeth inside the shell-mouth. Lives in drier places. Distribution: British Isles; elsewhere Europe and N.W. Africa.

16

17

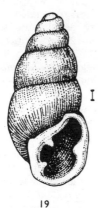

19

18

20. Two-toothed White Snail: *Leucophytia bidentata* (Montagu). Shell solid, spindle-shaped; body-whorl two-thirds of height; columellar lip thickened, with 2 strong folds projecting into mouth of shell; colour glossy white. H: 6 mm., B: 3 mm., W: 6–7. Near brackish water; estuaries and mud-flats. Distribution: coasts of E. and S.W. England, S. Wales and (discontinuous) Ireland; elsewhere W. and S. Europe, Atlantic Isles.

21. Mouse-ear-shelled Snail: *Phytia myosotis* (Draparnaud). Shell thin, forming a slightly to much broader spindle than *Leucophytia*; 3 tooth-folds from the columellar lip and 2 or 3 from the outer lip; colour brown or yellow. Mouth supposed to look like a mouse's ear. H: 8 mm., B: 3·5 mm., W: 7. Lives among rotting rubbish near high water along estuaries and mud-flats. Distribution: most coasts of England, Wales and Ireland, Firths of Forth, Solway and Moray; elsewhere W. Europe.

SUPERFAMILY LYMNAEACEA

Family Physidae (*Bladder Snails*)

Freshwater snails whose shells are always sinistral (coiled to the left) and narrow-mouthed. We have two British species.

22. Moss Bladder Snail: *Aplexa hypnorum* (L.). Shell sinistral, thin, glossy, transparent, elongate-oval; whorls slightly convex; body-whorl not swollen; mouth narrow, obliquely oval; peristome sharp, without a lip; umbilicus cleft, covered by reflected columellar lip; colour brownish. H: 12–13 mm., B: 5 mm., W: 6–7. Animal black, active, with slender tentacles. Shell not covered (cf. *Physa*). Lives in shallow ponds and ditches, often among flote-grass (*Glyceria fluitans*) and is resistant to drought. Distribution: local throughout British Isles, but absent from much of Wales and most of Scotland; elsewhere Holarctic (i.e. N. America, Europe, N. Asia).

23. Bladder Snail: *Physa fontinalis* (L.). Shell sinistral, very thin, glossy, brittle, transparent; spire short, blunt; body-whorl distended, three-quarters of height; mouth oval, blocked off by penultimate whorl; peristome sharp, without a lip; horn-coloured. H: 9–12 mm., B: 6–8 mm., W: 4. The edges of the mantle are extended to form a series of finger-shaped processes which, in the living animal, are reflected to embrace and largely cover the shell. Common on weeds in moving water. Distribution: Devon to Aberdeen, Ireland; elsewhere Holarctic (see above).

Several *Physa* spp. have been introduced into Britain, but even the experts are none too sure what they are or whence they came.

Family Lymnaeidae (*Pond Snails*)

Freshwater snails whose shells are normally dextral (coiled to the right) and have a pointed spire and more or less oval mouth. The tentacles are flattened and triangular, and there is a pallial lobe of the mantle which may act as a schnorkel (seen to right of shell in Figure 29). Our commonest water-snails, the 8 British species living on mud or weeds in most slow and standing waters. Some are economically important as intermediate hosts of liver flukes (*Distomum* spp.). Variously regarded as one genus (*Lymnaea*) or several; we will compromise and recognise 2 genera with 4 subgenera.

Myxas differs from *Lymnaea* in that the mantle completely envelops the shell.

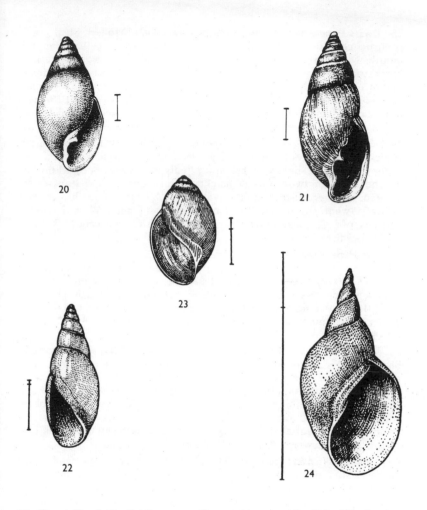

20

21

23

22

24

24. Great Pond Snail: *Lymnaea* (*Lymnaea*) *stagnalis* (**L.**). The largest species; spire relatively slender, tapering to a point; body-whorl distended, ovoid, more than two-thirds the height of the shell; growth-striations prominent; umbilicus blocked by reflected columellar lip; pale to dark horn-colour, often encrusted with coloured precipitates. H: 45–60 mm., B: 20–30 mm., W: 7–7½. Several named varieties and ecological forms; size of shell depends on volume of water in which animal develops. A tough customer; feeds on plants, detritus, is fond of carrion and attacks living snails, insect larvae, fish and newts! Prefers hard, slow or standing water. Distribution: England (except S.W.), Wales (except W.), Ireland except S.W.), Scottish Lowlands; elsewhere Holarctic (see previous page).

25. Dwarf Pond Snail: *Lymnaea* (*Galba*) *truncatula* (Müller). Shell small, elongate conical-ovoid; spire bluntly pointed, usually taller than the mouth; whorls well-arched, flattened above, regularly increasing; surface finely striated or encrusted; mouth bluntly pointed above; peristome simple; umbilicus open, slight; colour horny yellow. H: 8–12 mm., B: 4–6 mm., W: 5–6. Important as intermediate host of sheep liver-fluke (*Distomum hepaticum*). Ubiquitous in shallow, well-aerated waters; amphibious; resists drought. Distribution: throughout British Isles; elsewhere Holarctic.

26. Marsh Snail: *Lymnaea* (*Galba*) *palustris* (Müller). Shell medium-sized, elongate conical-ovoid; spire pointed (when not eroded) and about as tall as mouth; whorls slightly arched and rapidly increasing; body-whorl not distended, about two-thirds of height; surface spirally and transversely striated, often encrusted; mouth oval; no umbilicus; colour brown with yellowish-white suture. H: 20–30 mm., B: 10–14 mm., W: 6–7. Habits much as for *L.* (*G.*) *truncatula*. Distribution: British Isles except N.W. Scotland; elsewhere Holarctic.

27. Ear Pond Snail: *Lymnaea* (*Radix*) *auricularia* (L.). Shell large broad, thin, ear-shaped; spire a short, sharp cone, at most one-sixth of height; body-whorl very large and greatly distended; peristome strongly dilated; umbilicus cleft or covered; colour glossy brownish to whitish. H: 25–35 mm., B: 25–30 mm., W: 4–5. Prefers hard water; slow rivers, canals, large ponds. Distribution: Devon to Elgin, Ireland; elsewhere Palaearctic (i.e. Europe and N. Asia).

28. Wandering Snail: *Lymnaea* (*Radix*) *peregra* (Müller) **forma** *peregra*. Shell medium-sized, pointed, ovoid, strong-walled; spire conical and somewhat lower than the mouth; body-whorl not distended, but somewhat depressed laterally; mouth not sharp-pointed above; peristome simple and straightforward; umbilicus more or less covered; colour pale to dark horn-coloured. H: 15–20 mm., B: 12–13 mm., W: 4–5. Ubiquitous in slow and standing waters. Variable; many named varieties (see below). Distribution: British Isles; elsewhere Newfoundland, Europe, N. Asia.

29. *Lymnaea* (*Radix*) *peregra* (Müller) **forma** *ovata* Draparnaud. Shell medium-large ovoid, thin-walled; spire a short, blunt cone, at most one-quarter height; body-whorl large; mouth pointed above; peristome usually only distended below; umbilicus loosely covered; colour yellowish or reddish, often encrusted with black. H: 20–25 mm., B: 14–17 mm., W: 5. Habits and distribution: as for forma *peregra*.

30. North American Pond Snail: *Lymnaea* (*Stagnicola*) *catascopium* Say. Shell very variable, small to medium-large, short- to elongate-ovoid, rather like *L. peregra*, but narrower and with a sharper spire; spire dome-shaped to acutely conical; whorls well-rounded, sometimes stepped; body-whorl usually very large, moderately convex; suture slight to deep; mouth oval to elongate oval, as long or longer than spire; peristome sometimes so much expanded and reflected as to form a thick white rim, internally reinforced by chestnut lip and with a callus on the parietal wall; umbilicus reduced to a narrow cleft or wholly covered; surface smooth, dull to almost polished,

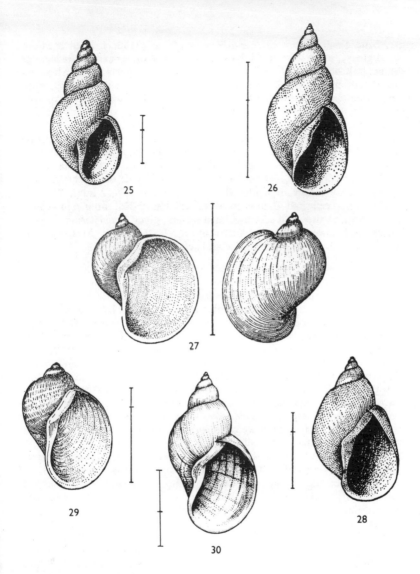

25

26

27

29

30

28

with fine to coarse striations (lens) and sometimes even ribbed; light horn-colour to dark chestnut. H: 9–20 mm., B: 5·5–11·5 mm., W: 5–6. Animal's body grey (dirty yellowish in *L. peregra*); tentacles long and pointed as in *L. palustris* (short and blunt in *L. peregra*), curved forwards. Species was introduced with Canadian birch-logs *c*. 1900–29, and flourishes in a warm engine pond at Leith at a temperature of 27° C. and population-density of 54 per sq. ft. Distribution: Leith; elsewhere eastern N. America.

31. Mud Snail: *Lymnaea* (*Leptolimnea*) *glabra* (Müller). Shell medium-sized glossy, more cylindrical than in any other *Lymnaea* sp.; spire slender, blunt, half height, with very regularly increasing whorls; body-whorl not distended; mouth small, pear-shaped; peristome with internal lip, outer and columellar lips almost parallel; umbilicus slight; colour brown or grey. H: 14–25 mm., B: 4–7 mm., W: 7–8. Local in small ponds and ditches, often those liable to dry out. Distribution: mainly N., E., S., and S.W. England, N.W. and S.W. Wales, Central Scotland; elsewhere W. Europe.

32. Glutinous Snail: *Myxas glutinosa* (Müller). *L. auricularia* carried to extremes! Shell small, bubble-thin, transparent; spire blunt, much shorter than other spp.; body-whorl huge, nearly spherical; mouth large, oval; colour glassy yellow or white. H: 13–15 mm., B: 10–12 mm., W: 5. In living animal reflected mantle almost covers whole shell (unique in family). Rare, local, in slow and standing hard waters; given to mysterious appearances and disappearances. Distribution: E. England, Midlands and Westmorland, N. and Central Ireland; elsewhere Europe.

Family Planorbidae (*Ram's-horn or Trumpet Snails*)

Common freshwater snails, having a sinistral (left-wound) shell coiled in one plane. The animal normally carries the shell upside-down; to establish the true relations, hold the shell with the mouth to the left, when the spire will be on the upper side and the umbilicus on the lower. The spire is commonly intorted or sunken, in some species to such a degree that the umbilicus is convex and one might believe the shell to be dextral. The tentacles are long and slender; the foot is rounded at both ends and there is a prominent lobe (inferior pallial lobe: see Figure 28) at the left side of the mantle serving as a gill. These snails are herbivores and more dependent on water-weeds than the Lymnaeidae; small species often float at the surface. *Valvata cristata* (*q.v.*, page 58) is the only British species likely to be confused with them. Again we compromise on nomenclature by recognising subgenera. There are 14 British species.

33. Great Ram's-horn Snail: *Planorbarius corneus* (L.). Largest species. Shell large, strong-walled, forms thick, flat disc; whorls well rounded, not keeled, increasing rapidly; suture deep; mouth broadly kidney-shaped; spire slightly sunken; umbilicus broad and deep; surface glossy, with close growth-lines, fine striations and locally pitted patches; colour red-brown to olive. H: 10–14 mm., B: 27–30 mm., W: 5–5½. Animal dark brown or (no body-pigment, blood-haemoglobin shows through) red. Egg-mass (20–40 eggs) as Figure 34c. Young shells hairy. Local; prefers hard, slow or standing, weedy waters. Distribution: England and Wales, except west coast counties; local in Ireland; elsewhere Europe to Central Asia.

34. Trumpet Ram's-horn Snail: *Menetus dilatatus* (Gould). Shell tiny, fairly thick-walled, forming a deeply biconcave disc; whorls flattened above, swollen below, increasing rapidly; suture deep; body-whorl sharp-edged above, enlarging to form trumpet-shaped mouth with expanded peristome; spire deeply sunken; umbilicus small, deep; surface wrinkled by growth-lines (lens!); colour yellowish-green. H: 1·2 mm., B: 3·7 mm., W: 3. Distribution: Loch a Mhuilinn, Raasay (apparently native), canals around Manchester (introduced with cotton-bales, 1869); elsewhere N. America.

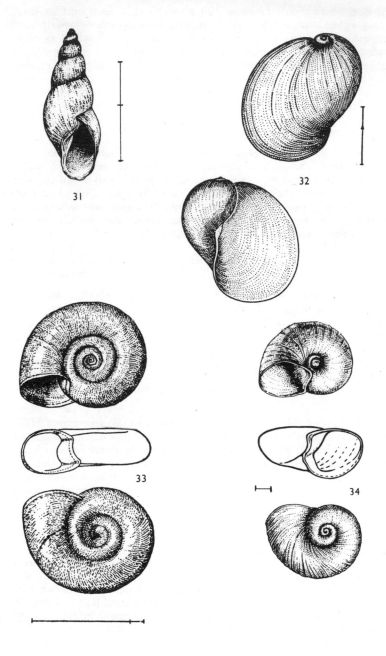

31

32

33

34

35. Ram's-horn Snail: *Planorbis* (*P.*) *planorbis* (**L.**). Shell medium-sized, strong-walled, forming a thickish, slightly biconcave disc; whorls more convex below than above, increasing gradually; body-whorl (greatest diameter one-quarter shell-breadth) with a thread-like keel towards the upper (spire) side; mouth rhomboidal to drop-shaped, slightly expanded, with a rib inside the peristome; spire slightly sunken; umbilicus deep; surface dull, finely striated; horn-colour. H: 3–3·5 mm., B: 14–17 mm., W: 5–6. Prefers hard, weedy waters, mainly ditches and small ponds. Distribution (except for some western counties) England, Wales and Ireland, Scottish Lowlands; elsewhere Europe to Central Asia, N. Africa.

36. Keeled Ram's-horn Snail: *Planorbis* (*P.*) *carinatus* **Müller.** Shell medium-sized, thin-walled, forming a thickish flattened disc; whorls equally convex on both sides, increasing rapidly; body-whorl (greatest diameter one-third shell-breadth) with a sharp (not thread-like) keel at the middle of the periphery or slightly towards the upper side; mouth heart-shaped; spire slightly sunken; umbilicus broad and shallow; surface glossy, finely striated; colour yellowish-grey. H: 2·5–3·5 mm., B: 14–17 mm., W: 4–5. Lives in hard, slow or standing, weedy waters, generally larger in area than *P. planorbis* frequents. Distribution: in British Isles as for *P. planorbis*, but less frequent in Scottish Lowlands; elsewhere Europe.

37. Whirlpool Ram's-horn Snail: *Planorbis* (*Anisus*) *vortex* (**L.**). Shell small, thin-walled, forming a very thin, flat disc; whorls flattened above, convex below; body-whorl with a sharp keel towards the upper (spire) side; mouth angular, twisted; spire flat or slightly sunken; umbilicus broad and shallow; surface finely and closely striated (lens!); pale horn-colour. H: 1–1·5 mm., B: 9–10 mm., W: 6–7. Prefers hard and flowing water; weedy rivers, canals and ponds. Distribution: England, E. Wales, local in Scotland, Shannon basin in Ireland; elsewhere Palaearctic (i.e. Europe and N. Asia).

38. White-lipped Ram's-horn Snail: *Planorbis* (*Anisus*) *leucostoma* **Millet.** Shell very small, fairly strong-walled, forming a thin disc more concave below than above; whorls flat above, convex below, increasing slowly and regularly; body-whorl with a blunt keel towards the upper (spire) side; mouth rounded-angular with a white rib; spire flat or slightly depressed; umbilicus broad and shallow; surface finely striated externally (lens!); colour horn-brown with a silky lustre. H: 1–1·5 mm., B: 5–8 mm., W: 6–7. Lives in ponds, ditches and marshes; resists drought in mud. Distribution: England, Wales, Ireland, sparser in N. Scotland; elsewhere Europe, W. Siberia.

39. Little Whirlpool Ram's-horn Snail: *Planorbis* (*Anisus*) *vorticulus* **Troschel.** Shell very small, thin-walled, forming a low, biconvex disc; whorls flattened with a median keel, increasing gradually; mouth oval; surface smooth and glossy; colour yellowish. H: 1 mm., B: 3·5–5 mm., W: 5. Among water-plants at the sides of ditches and marsh drains. Distribution: Sussex, E. Norfolk; elsewhere Holland to S. Russia.

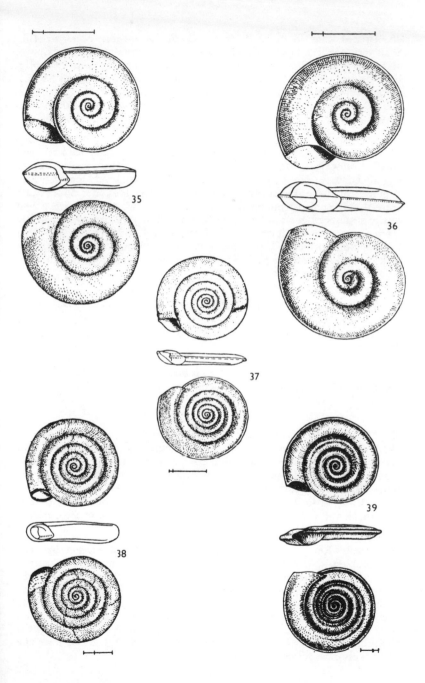

35

36

37

38

39

40. Twisted Ram's-horn Snail: *Planorbis* (*Bathyomphalus*) *contortus* (L.). Shell very small, rather strong-walled, forming a thick disc, concave above and flat below; whorls rounded, compact, increasing imperceptibly; suture deep; mouth crescentic; spire deeply sunken; umbilicus slight; surface very finely rib-striated (lens!); colour yellowish-brown. H: 1·7–2 mm., B: 5–6 mm., W: 7–8. In flowing and standing waters. Distribution: British Isles except Cornwall and S. Wales; elsewhere Europe to Siberia.

41. White Ram's-horn Snail: *Planorbis* (*Gyraulus*) *albus* Müller. Shell small, thin-walled, forming a thick disc deeply concave above, flat or slightly concave below; whorls well rounded, increasing very regularly and rapidly, usually not keeled, each overlapping the previous one; mouth oval; spire deeply sunken; umbilicus broad and shallow; surface with a fine lattice-structure (lens); colour translucent yellow-grey or greenish-white. Variable according to locality. H: 1·3–1·8 mm., B: 4–7 mm., W: 4–4½. No haemoglobin in blood. Lives among weeds in all fresh waters. Distribution: British Isles except N.W. Scotland; elsewhere Holarctic (i.e. Europe, N. Asia and N. America).

42. Smooth Ram's-horn Snail: *Planorbis* (*Gyraulus*) *laevis* Alder. Shell very small, thin-walled, forming a thick disc concave above and convex below; whorls well-rounded, increasing rapidly, close, never keeled; suture deep; mouth round, small; spire deeply sunken; umbilicus broad, shallow; surface smooth, apart from wrinkled growth-lines (lens!); colour translucent brownish. H: 1·5–2 mm., B: 5–6 mm., W: 3–4. Local on weeds in lakes and ponds, often near sea. Distribution: mainly N. England, sporadic in rest of British Isles; elsewhere Holarctic.

43. Thames Ram's-horn Snail: *Planorbis* (*Gyraulus*) *acronicus* Férussac. Shell small, thin-walled, forming a thick biconvex disc; whorls round above, flat below, increasing gradually, with a rough peripheral keel; mouth oval to round; spire sunken; umbilicus shallow; surface glossy with coarse transverse striations (lens!); colour brownish. H: 1·5 mm., B: 6–8 mm., W: 3½–4. In quiet, shallow backwaters; on algae and water-plants. Distribution: local in Thames Basin; elsewhere N. Europe to Switzerland.

44. Nautilus Ram's-horn Snail: *Planorbis* (*Gyraulus* or *Armiger*) *crista* (L.). Shell minute, thin-walled, forming a thick disc, concave above, convex below; whorls flattened, increasing rapidly, bluntly angular (rarely keeled), with curved transverse ridges forming points at the periphery; mouth round or oval; spire deeply sunken; umbilicus elevated; surface dull, finely striated (lens!); colour pale horn-brown. H: 0·5–1 mm., B: 2–3 mm., W: 3–4. The only species with the mantle-cavity always full of water. On plants in still or running waters. Distribution: British Isles except some western counties; elsewhere Holarctic.

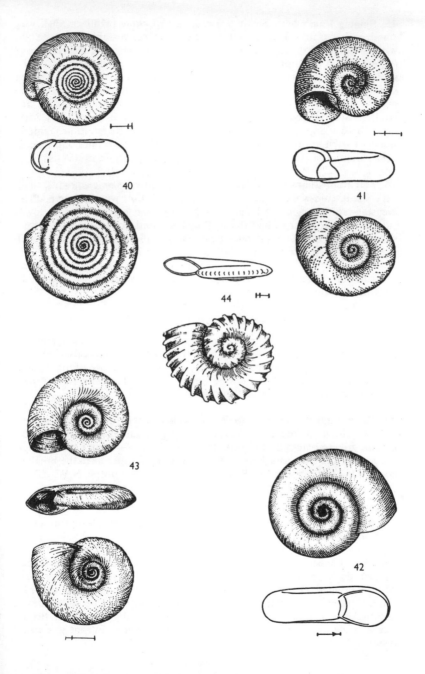

40

41

44

43

42

45. Shining Ram's-horn Snail: *Segmentina* (*S.*) *nitida* (**Müller**). Shell very small, rather thin-walled, forming a thick disc, convex above, flat below; whorls flat above, convex below, each overlapping the previous one (especially on the upper (spire) side); body-whorl forming most of the shell, internally constricted at intervals by trios of enamel-ridges which show white through the shell; mouth heart-shaped or arrow-shaped; spire deeply sunken; umbilicus slightly depressed; surface glossy, with fine striations (lens!); colour yellow-brown with a reddish tinge. H: 1·7–1·8 mm., B: 6–7 mm., W: 4½–5. Local in ponds and marsh-drains among weeds. Distribution: mainly S. and E. England to Yorkshire and Lancashire, Glamorgan, Montgomery; elsewhere Europe to Central Asia.

46. Flat Ram's-horn Snail: *Segmentina* (*Hippeutis*) *complanata* (**L.**). Shell very small, thin-walled, forming a lens-shaped disc; whorls flattened, increasing rapidly, each overlapping the previous one, especially on the lower side; body-whorl forms half the shell and is bluntly keeled; mouth arrow-shaped; spire sunken; umbilicus broad and shallow; surface glossy, with fine irregular striations (lens); colour yellowish-horny to grey-white. H: 1–1·2 mm., B: 2–3 mm., W: 3–4. Prefers hard water; ponds and ditches. Distribution: Great Britain (except Cornwall, W. and N. Scotland), Ireland; elsewhere Palaearctic.

Family Ancylidae (*River Limpets*)

Shell conical-depressed, not coiled (though the embryonic shell and soft parts of the adult show that the animals are actually sinistral). Tentacles short, flat; foot large; no mantle-cavity: inferior pallial lobe of mantle acts as gill. (No relation to the marine limpets (Patellidae) which are Prosobranchiata.) We have one British species.

47. River Limpet: *Ancylus fluviatilis* **Müller.** Shell thin-walled, bonnet-shaped, with a hooked apex inclined to the right, but no spire. Mouth oval. Colour grey to black. L: 4–9 mm., B: 3–7 mm., H: 2–5 mm. Feeds on algal scum, etc., and lives attached to stones in running water or in the breaker-zone of lakes. Distribution: British Isles; elsewhere Europe, N.W. Africa.

Family Acroloxidae (*Lake Limpets*)

Similar to the Ancylidae (above), but dextral and with a less pronounced apex to the shell. We have one British species.

48. Lake Limpet: *Acroloxus lacustris* (**L.**). Shell delicate, elongate shield-shaped, flatly arched; apex hardly apparent, inclined to the left; no spire. Mouth elongate-elliptical to bluntly rectangular. L: 7 mm., B: 3 mm., H: 2 mm. Prefers hard water; lives attached to plant-stems or undersides of floating leaves in slow and standing waters. Distribution: Great Britain (rarer in the west and north), Ireland (ditto); elsewhere Europe to Central Asia.

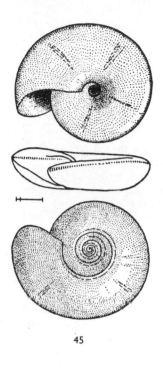

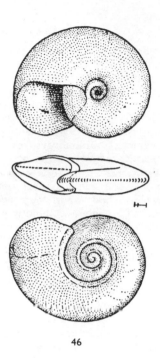

45

46

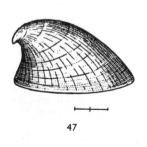

47

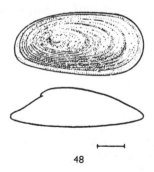

48

SUPERFAMILY SUCCINEACEA

Family *Succineidae* (*Amber Snails*)

Shell dextral, very thin, glossy, yellow, ovoid, mostly body-whorl, with a pointed spire, an oval mouth, a sharp, simple, unreflected peristome and no umbilicus. The animal is very soft, looks a size too large for its shell (elsewhere the family has given rise to slug-like forms), and has reduced anterior tentacles, separate male and female openings and a jaw with a chisel-shaped dorsal appendage. The Succineidae live on and among waterside plants. While family identification is for once possible on shell-characters, variability makes species identification far less certain. Our five species are here arranged according to increasing size of spire.

49. Amber Snail: *Succinea putris* (L.). Shell thin, translucent, ovoid (H: 1·6–1·8 × B), with a short spire; whorls somewhat rounded, increasing rapidly; body-whorl very swollen, four-fifths of height; suture deep; mouth broadly oval, bluntly pointed above, two-thirds of height; surface glossy, very finely striated (lens); pale yellow or dull horn-coloured. H: 17–24 mm., B: 10–13 mm., W: 4. Animal typically yellowish-grey, but sometimes dark. Lives in marshes and along river and lake banks on and among waterside plants. The tentacles are often swollen, and brightly coloured with the encysted larvae of the fluke *Distomum macrostomum*, which completes its life-cycle in birds; the latter peck off the tentacles and become infected, while the snail grows replacements! Distribution: England, Wales and Ireland; Scottish records uncertain; elsewhere Europe, except Mediterranean region.

50. Pfeiffer's Amber Snail: *Succinea pfeifferi* Rossmässler. Shell small, thin, not very translucent, elongate-ovoid (H: 1·6–2·2 × B), with a short spire; whorls rather flattened, increasing rapidly; body-whorl seven-tenths of height; suture deep; mouth drop-shaped, bluntly pointed above, about four-sevenths of height; surface with irregular, not very strong striations; colour bright pale amber to reddish-amber. H: 10 mm., B: 6 mm., W: 3. Animal typically dark, spotted with black, but sometimes light. Habits as for *S. putris*. Distribution: British Isles; elsewhere Europe, Asia Minor, N.W. Africa.

51. Slender Amber Snail: *Succinea elegans* Risso. Shell fairly thick, somewhat translucent, elongate (H: 2·1–2·4 × B), with a moderate spire; whorls rather flattened, increasing rapidly; body-whorl narrow, but four-fifths of height; mouth rectangular-oval, sharply pointed above, two-thirds of height; surface with deep, regular striations (lens); colour pale to deep amber. H: 15 mm., B: 6·2 mm., W: 3–3½. Animal dark. Lives in swamps, marshes, along river banks and on floating leaves, in wetter situations than the other spp. Distribution: Norfolk, Herts.; elsewhere N. Europe.

52. Small Amber Snail: *Succinea oblonga* (Draparnaud). Shell small, thick, elongate (H: 2–2·1 × B), with a rather produced spire; whorls well rounded, increasing gradually; body-whorl half of height; suture very deep; mouth broadly elliptical, bluntly pointed above, three-sevenths of height; surface

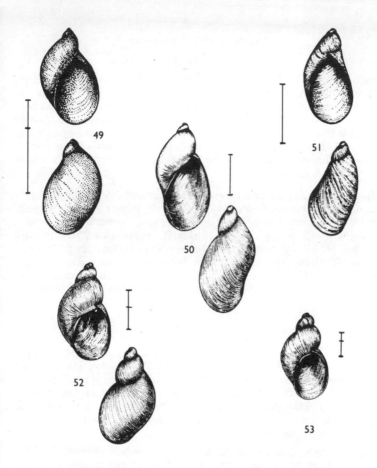

slightly glossy, with strong irregular striations; colour dull greenish-yellow to reddish-brown. H: 6–10 mm., B: 3–5 mm., W: 4. Animal light to dark grey. Rare and local in marshes and at sides of ditches. Distribution: coastal counties of British Isles; elsewhere Europe, more local in the south.

53. Sand-bowl Amber Snail: *Catinella arenaria* **(Bouchard-Chantereaux).** Shell small, thick, conical-ovate to subconical globose, with a produced, blunt spire; whorls swollen, increasing gradually; body-whorl one-half of height; suture very deep; mouth pear-shaped, three-sevenths of height; surface with rather coarse, irregular striations (lens); colour reddish-amber. H: 4·5–6 mm., B: 3–3·6 mm., W: 4. Animal pale grey to black. Very rare, in wet hollows in sand-dunes. Distribution: N. Devon, Central and W. Ireland; elsewhere W. Europe.

Family Pyramidulidae (*Rock Snails*)

Small, primitive land-snails, impossible to define in non-technical terms, and presenting the further difficulty that their shells alone among the primitive families assume the conventional **Helix** shape. The thickness, colour and number of whorls in such a tiny shell will serve to distinguish a **Pyramidula** from the young of many larger species, but the beginner had better check any suspect specimen against illustrations of the smaller Valloniidae, Enodontidae, Zonitidae, Vitrinidae and Helicidae. We have only one British species.

54. Rock Snail: *Pyramidula rupestris* (Draparnaud). Shell dextral, very small, fairly thick-walled, bluntly top-shaped; whorls swollen, stepped against one another; suture deep; mouth round; peristome thin, sharp; surface finely and closely rib-striated (lens!), slightly glossy; colour dark red-brown. H: 1·5–1·8 mm., B: 2·5–3 mm., W: 4–4½. Lives in dry sites on rocks, cliffs, walls, etc., especially in limestone country. Distribution: England (except E.), W. and S. Wales, Central Scotland, Ireland (except N.E.); elsewhere Europe (except N. and E.), Asia Minor, N.W. Africa.

Family Cochlicopidae (*Agate Snails*)

Shell dextral, glossy (Agate or Slippery Snails), broadly or narrowly spindle-shaped, with a long spire and blunt apex; columella often shortened or folded. Median teeth on radula tiny; lateral and marginal teeth large and 3-pointed. *Azeca* has teeth around the peristome and carries its shell horizontally; *Cochlicopa* has a smooth peristome and carries its shell obliquely. The animals live in damp leaf-mould, moss, etc. (Moss Snails). We have 3 British species.

55. Three-toothed Snail/Moss Snail: *Azeca goodalli* (Férussac). Shell plumply spindle- or chrysalis-shaped, smooth, glossy, translucent, with slightly convex whorls, a shallow suture and a blunt apex; peristome with a thickened, inturned lip; mouth obliquely pear-shaped, constricted by 3 irregular teeth arising, 1 each, from the outer, columellar and parietal lips (further teeth may be present, as figured); colour yellowish or pale reddish-brown. H: 5·5–6·5 mm., B: 2·5–2·7 mm., W: 7. Locally numerous, in leaf-mould under woods and hedges. Distribution: England (except most of S.W.), Wales, (except S.W.), Perthshire; elsewhere W. Europe.

56. Slippery Snail/Moss Snail: *Cochlicopa lubrica* (Müller). Shell elongate-ovoid, smooth, glossy, transparent, with fairly convex whorls, a moderate suture and a blunt apex; peristome blunt with an internal rib; mouth oval without tooth-formations; colour yellowish to reddish horn-brown. H: 5–7 mm., B: 2·5–3 mm., W: 5½–6. Ubiquitous in moss, dead leaves, turf, rotten wood, etc., in damp or even saturated sites. Distribution: British Isles; elsewhere Holarctic (i.e. N. America, Europe, N. Asia).

Plate I. Large Red Slug, *Arion ater rufus* (L.), about life-size (*see* p. 100). Note the position of the respiratory opening on the right side before the centre of the mantle-shield, the keel-less back and the wide foot-fringe—all characteristics of the Family Arionidae (cf. Plate II). Note also the open and closed conditions of the respiratory opening. *Arion Ater* is a very variable slug, exhibiting a complete range of colour-shades all the way from the black or dark brown *A. a. ater* with the grey sole to the bright reddish or yellowish *A. a. rufus* with the creamy-yellow one. Except that *A. a. ater* seldom has a brightly coloured foot-fringe there is no certain way of distinguishing between the two forms without examining small details of their internal anatomy. (Photos by Dr. Helmut Länge.)

Plate II. Great Grey Slug, *Limax maximus* L., somewhat enlarged (*see* p. 103). Note the position of the respiratory opening on the right side behind the centre of the mantle-shield, the partly-keeled back and narrow foot-fringe—all characteristics of the Family Limacidae (cf. Plate I). (Photo. by W. Harstrick.)

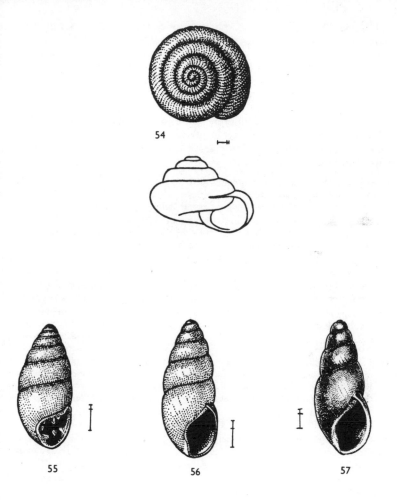

54

55   56   57

57. Least Slippery Snail/Moss Snail: *Cochlicopa minima* **(Siemaschko).**
Shell differs from previous in small size, more cylindrical form, less convex
whorls, broader and more rounded apex and narrower mouth; colour
lighter, more violet. H: 4–5·2 mm., B: 1·9–2·2 mm., W: 5–5½. Distribution:
British Isles, probably as general as previous species, but records still incomplete; elsewhere Europe.

Family Vertiginidae (*Whorl Snails and Chrysalis Snails*)

(Includes the Pupillidae of other classifications.) Small to tiny land-snails, whose shells are usually dextral (right-wound), but sometimes sinistral, cylindrical, dumpy or globular in form, with a fairly elongate and prominent spire and a mouth often guarded against insect enemies by a palisade of teeth which makes a good substitute for an operculum. The anterior tentacles are short or absent. A more precise definition would require more knowledge of anatomy and skill at dissection than can be assumed here. The reader should therefore compare his specimens with the illustrations of the families Cochlicopidae, Vertiginidae and Enidae, and, if they seem to resemble the Vertiginidae, use the following key. We have 16 British species.

1. Mouth with 4 or more very obvious teeth............................ 2
   Mouth with less than 4 teeth.. 3
   (Test also 2c–7–9 for Central Ireland specimens)
2. Whorls 8–10; height more than twice breadth; 6–8 mm.......... *Abida secale*
   Whorls 6–7; height less than twice breadth; 4 mm............. *Lauria anglica*
   Whorls 4–5; height less than twice breadth; 2–2·5 mm. (*Vertigo*).......... 7
3. No teeth in mouth (examine inside carefully)......................... 4
   1 to 3 teeth in mouth.. 5
4. Shell cylindrical; height more than twice breadth...... *Truncatellina cylindrica*
   Shell subcylindrical; height not more than twice breadth....*Columella edentula*
5. A blunt tooth inside the body-whorl, visible through the mouth; 1 parietal and
   1 columellar tooth, visible when the shell is viewed obliquely; shell cylindrical
   .... *Truncatellina britannica*
   No tooth inside body-whorl... 6
6. Peristome reflected; insertion of columellar lip turns away from mouth; parietal
   lip conspicuous; usually 1 parietal tooth................. *Lauria cylindracea*
   Peristome not reflected; columellar lip continues circle of peristome; parietal lip
   inconspicuous; usually 1 parietal tooth................... *Pupilla muscorum*
7. Shell sinistral 8
   Shell dextral 9
8. Mouth nearly triangular; 4–5 teeth...................... *Vertigo angustior*
   Mouth nearly rectangular; 6–7 teeth........................... *V. pusilla*
9. Outer lip strongly arched towards insertion; mouth round; 0–4 teeth.........
   .... *Vertigo genesii*
   Outer lip not strongly arched...................................... 10
10. Body-whorl more than twice height of spire............. *Vertigo moulinsiana*
    Body-whorl not more than twice height of spire...................... 11
11. Penultimate whorl broader than body-whorl; 4–6 teeth...... *Vertigo substriata*
    Penultimate whorl less broad than body-whorl........................ 12
12. 6–8 teeth... *Vertigo antivertigo*
    Usually less than 6 teeth.. 13
13. Breadth two-thirds height; 4 teeth....................... *Vertigo lilljeborgi*
    Breadth less than two-thirds height................................ 14
14. Shell yellowish, strongly striated; 4 teeth.................... *Vertigo alpestris*
    Shell brownish, hardly striated; 4–5 teeth..................... *V. pygmaea*

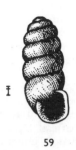

58   59   60

58. Toothless Chrysalis Snail: *Columella edentula* **(Draparnaud).** Shell thin-walled, conical barrel-shaped, with a rounded apex; whorls rounded, increasing slowly; suture deep; mouth rounded, almost as broad as tall, without tooth-formations; peristome without a strengthening lip, not dilated; umbilicus finely perforate; surface glossy with faint striations (lens!); colour pale horn-brown. H: 2·3–2·6 mm., B: 1·3–1·4 mm., W: 6–6½. General in woods, marshes, damp places with clumps of herbage, especially butterbur (*Petasites hybridus*). Distribution: most of British Isles; elsewhere Holarctic (i.e. Europe, N. Asia and N. America).

59. Cylindrical Whorl Snail: *Truncatellina cylindrica* **(Férussac).** Shell cylindrical, with a blunt apex; whorls rounded; suture deep; mouth oblique-oval, without tooth-formations; peristome dilated and feebly reinforced by a lip; umbilicus cleft or very finely perforate; surface glossy with 30 fine ribs per millimetre (lens!); pale horn-colour. H: 1·6–2·2 mm., B: 0·8–1·0 mm., W: 6–7. Rare and local on dry, glassy slopes, sandhills, coastal turf or among withered plants at the foot of chalk cliffs. Distribution: sporadic in E. England and E. Scotland; elsewhere Europe, Asia Minor, N.W. Africa.

60. British Whorl Snail: *Truncatellina britannica* **Pilsbry.** Shell cylindrical, shorter than the above, with a more domed apex; whorls rounded; suture deep; mouth oblique-oval, with a tooth well inside the parietal wall, another well inside the columellar lip and a third on the inside of the shell, visible through the mouth; peristome slightly dilated with a thickened lip; umbilicus covered; surface glossy with 20 fine ribs per millimetre (lens!); colour cinnamon. H: 1·74 mm., B: 0·85 mm., W: 5½. Lives on dry chalk and limestone country near the sea. Distribution: southern coast of Devon, Dorset and Isle of Wight; apparently endemic (i.e. confined to this region).

61. Narrow-mouthed Whorl Snail: *Vertigo angustior* Jeffreys. Shell sinistral, elliptical, tapering towards mouth; spire short and blunt; whorls convex, compressed, increasing gradually; suture fairly deep; mouth a right-angled triangle, with typically 4 teeth (2 parietal, 1 columellar, 1–2 outer); peristome with a thickened lip, slightly dilated; umbilicus cleft; surface glossy with fine close striations (lens!); light horn-colour. H: 1·6–1·8 mm., B: 0·8–0·9 mm., W: 4½–5. Rare and local, in damp moss and grass on marshes or among flood debris. Distribution: E. England, N. and S. Wales, Sutherland, more frequent in Ireland; elsewhere Europe, except Mediterranean countries.

62. Wall Whorl Snail: *Vertigo pusilla* Müller. Shell sinistral; more elongate than the above, but broader towards the mouth; spire nearly as tall as body-whorl; whorls swollen; suture deep; mouth a battered rectangle, with typically 6 teeth (2 parietal, 2 columellar, 2–3 outer); peristome with a thickened lip, slightly dilated; umbilicus cleft; surface glossy, with faint striations (lens!); colour yellowish to white. H: 2 mm., B: 1 mm., W: 5. Lives amongst moss, dead leaves or ivy on old walls and dry banks. Distribution: N. Devon and Berkshire to N. England, N. Wales, local from S.W. Scotland to Elgin, Ireland (Wexford, Limerick, Galway, Kerry); elsewhere Europe.

63. Common Whorl Snail: *Vertigo pygmaea* (Draparnaud). Our commonest *Vertigo* sp. Shell dextral, cylindrical ovoid; spire fairly tall; whorls moderately convex, the body-whorl with a strong, rounded crest a short distance behind the peristome; suture fairly deep; mouth quadrangular pear-shaped, with typically 4 teeth (1 parietal, 1 columellar, 2–3 outer, the last on a common ridge); umbilicus deeply cleft; surface glossy with faint striations and microscopic pitting (lens!); colour brown. H: 1·9–2·2 mm., B: 1·1–1·2 mm., W: 5. Amongst grass and moss, or under wood or stones in meadows, marshes and cultivated lands. Distribution: British Isles, except part of Scottish Highlands; elsewhere Europe into Asia, Asia Minor, Atlantic Islands, N. America.

64. Mountain Whorl Snail: *Vertigo alpestris* Alder. Shell dextral, more cylindrical than *V. pygmaea*; spire shorter, with a blunter apex; whorls more rounded, body-whorl without crest; suture deep; mouth semicircular, with 4 teeth (1 parietal, 1 columellar, 2 outer); peristome reflected; surface glossy with strong transverse striations (lens!); colour pale yellowish. H: 2 mm., B: 1 mm., W: 5. Local on rocks and stone walls in high limestone districts. Distribution: N. England, N. Wales, Mull; elsewhere mountainous regions of Canada, Newfoundland, N. Europe, Siberia.

65. Round-mouthed Whorl Snail: *Vertigo genesii* Gredler. Shell dextral, small, ovoid; spire with flattened apex, looks top-heavy owing to largish penultimate whorl; whorls rounded; suture deep; mouth rounded with 0–4 small teeth (1 parietal, 1 columellar, 1–2 outer); peristome thickened, blue-black, outer lip well arched (quadrant) towards insertion; umbilicus moderate; surface glossy, more striated than *V. pygmaea* (lens!); colour purplish-brown (animal black). H: 1·5 mm., B: 1 mm., W: 4½. Local on damp ground at margins of peat bogs on limestone. Distribution: Central Ireland; elsewhere N. Europe to Siberia.

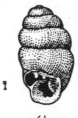

61

62

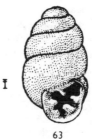

63

64

65

66. Striated Whorl Snail: *Vertigo substriata* (**Jeffreys**). Shell dextral, broadly spindle-shaped; spire short, blunt; whorls well rounded, the penultimate almost swollen and slightly broader than the body-whorl; suture very deep; mouth semi-oval, with typically 4–5 teeth (1–3 parietal, 1 columellar, 2–3 outer); peristome with a rib; umbilicus cleft; surface glossy, more strongly striated on the spire (lens!); colour yellowish to white. H: 1·75–2 mm., B: 1 mm., W: 4½. Lives in moss, grass-roots or under stones in damp situations. Distribution: Devon to Sutherland (rare north of Stafford), Ireland; elsewhere Europe.

67. Marsh Whorl Snail: *Vertigo antivertigo* (**Draparnaud**). The first of 3 species in which the body-whorl is large and the general form globular. Shell dextral, broadly ovoid, flattened below; spire obliquely domed with a rounded apex; whorls rounded, body-whorl about twice height of spire; suture fairly deep; mouth pear-shaped, with typically 6 teeth (2 parietal, 2 columellar, 2–4 outer); peristome with rib, slightly reflected; umbilicus cleft; surface smooth, glossy; colour dark brown. H: 2 mm., B: 1·25 mm., W: 4–5. Lives in marshy places among dead vegetation or under stones, etc. Distribution: most of British Isles; elsewhere Europe into Asia, N.W. Africa.

68. Desmoulins' Whorl Snail: *Vertigo moulinsiana* (**Depuy**). Shell dextral, ovoid; spire obliquely domed with a rounded apex; whorls swollen, especially the body-whorl, which is slightly more than twice the height of the spire; suture deep; mouth (as occluded by outer tooth-ridge) elliptical, with typically 4 teeth (1 parietal, 1 columellar, 2–3 outer, the last joined by a tall ridge); peristome broad, white, inflected; umbilicus cleft; surface smooth, glossy, with very faint striations (lens!); colour yellowish. H: 2·3 mm., B: 1·45 mm., W: 4. Local in fens and marshes, on stems and bases of reeds, etc., but avoids damp and decaying matter. Distribution: E. (Broads, common) and S. England, Clare, Tipperary, Leinster; elsewhere Europe.

69. Lilljeborg's Whorl Snail: *Vertigo lilljeborgi* **Westerlund**. Shell dextral, ovoid; spire domed, blunt; whorls rounded, increasing rapidly; suture deep; mouth pear-shaped, typically with 4–5 teeth (1–2 parietal, 1–2 columellar, 2 outer); peristome thin, dilated; umbilicus narrowly cleft; surface very glossy, with fine striations (lens!); colour chestnut. H: 2–2·25 mm., B: 1·25–1·5 mm., W: 5. Lives among rotting drift vegetation on stony lake shores. Distribution: Lake District, Scotland, W. Ireland; elsewhere Pyrenees and N. Europe.

70. Large Chrysalis Snail: *Abida secale* (**Draparnaud**). Shell chrysalis-shaped; spire long, conical, pointed; whorls convex, increasing gradually; suture moderate; mouth elliptical, typically with 8–9 tooth-folds (2–3 parietal, 2 columellar, 4 outer); peristome dilated, with a brownish-white lip; umbilicus narrow, in a funnel-shaped depression; surface rib-striated (lens); colour brown or grey-brown. H: 6–8 mm., B: 2·5–3 mm., W: 9–10. Lives on rocks, hillsides, dry woods in limestone areas. Distribution: England (except eastern counties); elsewhere Europe (except Scandinavia and Mediterranean countries).

66

67

68

69

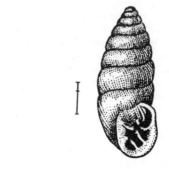

70

71. Moss Snail: *Pupilla muscorum* **(L.).** Shell strong-walled, cylindrical, with a nearly hemispherical apex; whorls convex; suture slight; mouth small, round, with a small parietal tooth and a broad white ridge inside the outer lip; peristome dilated and reinforced; umbilicus cleft, in a funnel-shaped depression; surface faintly glossy, finely striated (lens!); colour reddish horn-brown (empty shells paler, yellow-brown to white). H: 3–3·5 mm., B: 1·5–1·8 mm., W: 6–7. Lives in short turf, loose stones, walls, rocks, etc. Distribution: British Isles, sparse in Scotland; elsewhere Holarctic.

72. Chrysalis Snail: *Lauria cylindracea* **(da Costa).** Shell thin, transparent, cylindrical with a tapering, conical spire; whorls convex, increasing gradually; suture deep; mouth oval, with 1 (rarely 0 or 2) parietal tooth; peristome dilated, with a broad, white lip; umbilicus narrow, but open; surface smooth, glossy, with almost imperceptible striations (lens!); colour brown or white. H: 3·5–4 mm., B: 1·8–2 mm., W: 7. Common in woods, hedges, on walls, etc. Distribution: British Isles; elsewhere Europe, N. Africa, Madeira.

73. English Chrysalis Snail: *Lauria anglica* **(Wood).** Shell shorter, more oval and blunter than the above; whorls flatter, increasing more gradually still; suture shallower; mouth triangular pear-shaped, with 4 teeth (2 parietal, 1 columellar, 1 outer), inwardly directed; peristome reflected, with a thick lip and a projection from the outer lip towards the parietal tooth; umbilicus deep; surface glossy, more striated (lens!); horn-coloured. H: 3·75 mm., B: 2 mm., W: 6–7. Damp sites in woods, walls, hedges, etc. Distribution: north of line Humber–Ribble, rarer to the south, Ireland; elsewhere Portugal, Algeria.

Family Valloniidae (Grass Snails)

Small, dextral, umbilicate land-snails, intermediate between the Pyramidulidae and the Helicidae, and resembling the latter in the possession of a dart-sac which secretes a love-dart. The shell approaches the typical *Helix*-shape, the whorls are swollen and stepped and the mouth is round with a more or less thickened and reflected peristome, but no tooth-folds. *Vallonia* spp. do shun woods, but are by no means confined to grassland. We have 2 British genera and 5 species. *Vallonia* has a pale, smooth, squat shell, mostly body-whorl, with a broad umbilicus; *Acanthinula* has a darker, taller, top-shaped shell, with strong transverse ridges (which may bear spines) and a narrower umbilicus.

74. Ribbed Grass Snail: *Vallonia costata* **(Müller).** Shell tiny, flattened, almost circular in outline, with a rather depressed spire; suture deep; body-whorl large and swollen; mouth round; peristome sharp, reflected, with a strong white lip internally; umbilicus wide, funnel-shaped; surface with regular cuticular ribs, which may be abraded, but always remain recognisable (lens!); colour yellowish-grey. H: 1·2–1·3 mm., B: 2·5–2·7 mm., W: 3–4. Common among dead leaves and grass, on walls, etc., in dry situations. Distribution: England, Wales, Ireland, E. Scotland north to Aberdeen; elsewhere Holarctic (i.e. Europe, N. Asia, N. America).

71

72

73

74

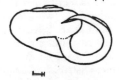

75. Smooth or Beautiful Grass Snail: *Vallonia pulchella* (Müller). Shell tiny, transparent, flattened, broadly elliptical in outline, with a slightly elevated conical spire; suture deep; body-whorl large, swollen, flattened above; mouth round; peristome blunt, reflected, with a strong lip; umbilicus broad, funnel-shaped, suddenly and considerably enlarged by the last quarter-whorl; surface finely striated (lens!); colour yellowish-grey to white. H: 1·2–1·3 mm., B: 2·5 mm., W: 3–4. Habitats similar to *V. costata*, but damper. Distribution: British Isles; elsewhere Holarctic.

76. Eccentric Grass Snail: *Vallonia excentrica* Sterki. Shell tiny, transparent or translucent, flattened, broadly elliptical in outline, with a depressed spire (about intermediate between *V. costata* and *V. pulchella*); mouth rounded, slightly dilated; peristome hardly reflected, with an internal lip; umbilicus less open than in *V. pulchella*, and suddenly and considerably enlarged by the last one-third whorl; surface smooth, glossy; colour pale yellow. H: 1·1 mm., B: 2·3 × 1·8 mm., W: 3–3½. Lives among grass-roots, moss, under stones, etc., in dry localities. Distribution: British Isles; elsewhere Holarctic.

77. Prickly Snail: *Acanthinula aculeata* (Müller). Shell tiny, spherical-conical, with a bluntly pointed, conical spire; whorls swollen and bearing conspicuous cuticular ribs, each of which is radially produced into a sharp peripheral spine; mouth semicircular; peristome expanded all around, faced internally with a thin white lip; umbilicus open; dark horn-colour to brown. H: 1·8–2·1 mm., B: 2–2·3 mm., W: 4. General under dead leaves, rotten wood, etc., in woods and hedges. Distribution: British Isles; elsewhere Europe to the Caucasus, N.W. Africa, Azores.

78. Plated or Plaited Snail: *Acanthinula lamellata* (Jeffreys). Shell tiny, thin-walled, spherical, with a low arched spire, altogether more globose than the above; whorls rounded, increasing gradually; suture deep; mouth semilunar; peristome thin; umbilicus narrow and deep; surface silky, with ribs and striations (lens!), but no spines; colour yellowish or tawny. H: 2 mm., B: 2–2·3 mm., W: 6. Local in old woods among dead leaves, etc. Distribution: mainly N. England, Scotland, Ireland, very sparse in S. England and Wales; elsewhere Holland to Scandinavia and E. Prussia.

Family Enidae (Bulins)

Land-snails with a dextral or sinistral conical-oval shell having a rather lengthy blunt spire, an oval mouth (with or without tooth-folds) and a thick peristome and narrow umbilicus. The tentacles are short and the radular teeth turn outwards. The peculiar "popular" name is apparently derived from *bulinus*, a little bubble or blister. Our two species are few and rather unrepresentative as compared with the Continental European fauna.

79. Bulin or Mountain Bulin: *Ena montana* (Draparnaud). Shell small to medium-sized, dextral, thin-walled, oval, with a blunt conical spire; whorls moderately rounded, body-whorl half height; mouth oval, without tooth-folds; peristome sharp, broadly reflected, faced with a smooth white lip; umbilicus cleft, narrow; surface glossy, criss-crossed with fine spiral and

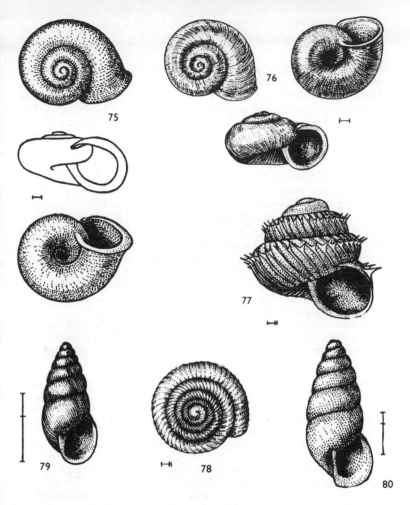

transverse striations, giving a granulated appearance (lens!); colour pale to dark horn-brown, peristome sometimes tinged with purple, inside brown. H: 12–18 mm., B: 5–6 mm., W: 7–8. Local among dead leaves in old woods (especially beech) and hedges in limestone country; climbs tree-trunks in wet weather. Distribution: S. England, Cork; elsewhere Central and W. Europe.

80. Lesser Bulin: *Ena obscura* (Müller). Differs from above in smaller size, more regularly increasing whorls, straighter outer edge to columellar lip, faint, irregular striations without granulation (lens!), duller gloss and paler colour. H: 8–11 mm., B: 3·5–4·5 mm., W: 7. Similar habits to *E. montana*, but much more widely distributed. Distribution: British Isles, except much of N. and W. Scotland and N. Ireland; elsewhere Europe, N.W. Africa.

Family Clausiliidae (Door Snails)

Small land-snails whose shells are normally sinistral, elongate and club-shaped, being somewhat swollen in the middle and tapered at both ends; the first 1–3 whorls form a blunt cylindrical "handle" to the club, while the body-whorl is rather slenderer than those immediately preceding it. The mouth is fundamentally pear-shaped, apart from sundry folds, etc., but drawn out into a jug-lip-like sinus at the upper outer corner. The peristome has a continuous and complete lip.

We have already noticed various forms of mouth-folds and teeth in members of the families Cochlicipidae, Vertiginidae and Enidae, devices which apparently protect these non-operculate snails from the attacks of soil-dwelling beetles. Here this tendency is carried still further. The parietal lip bears a pair of oblique folds which spiral into the interior of the shell, and the groove between these folds accommodates a sliding tongue-shaped or spoon-shaped door, the clausilium. There are further folds on the columellar and outer lips, two of which sometimes curve to meet one another and form a structure called a lunella. One of our species, appropriately named *Balea perversa*, lacks these mouth-modifications, but otherwise has a similarly shaped shell and shares the peculiarities of the reproductive organs characteristic of the family.

The Clausiliidae typically lie up in crevices and among debris during the day, and sally forth at night to climb tree-trunks and rocks in search of the lichens and mosses on which they feed. A key to our 4 genera and 6 species follows:

1. No clausilium; mouth of shell without folds or teeth, or at most with 1 small parietal tooth; H: 8–9 mm., W: 6–8............................***Balea perversa***
   Clausilium present; mouth of shell with 2 oblique parietal folds and various other folds and teeth; H: 11–19 mm., W: 9–13........................... 2
2. Umbilicus broad and shallow; mouth of shell with a narrow jug-lip at the lower extremity; whorls with very deep and regular transverse striations, the ridges half-white...***Laciniaria biplicata***
   Umbilicus narrow, cleft; lower part of mouth smoothly rounded; striations never as regular or deep as in the above; ridges not white...................... 3
3. Clausilium deeply notched at lower margin...............***Marpessa laminata***
   Clausilium not notched (***Clausilia***)................................... 4
4. Surface of shell finely granular (criss-crossed by transverse and spiral striations)
   .... ***Clausilia bidentata***
   Surface not granular, lacking spiral striations.......................... 5
5. Shell stouter, mouth broad; H: 12 mm., W: 9–11; in S. and C. England........
   ....***Clausilia rolphii***
   Shell slenderer, mouth narrow; H: 11–16 mm., W: 10–12; in N. England.......
   ....***C. dubia***

81. Plaited Door Snail: *Marpessa laminata* (Montagu). Shell sinistral, thin-walled, translucent, club-shaped; whorls rounded, the first 4 forming a cylinder; body-whorl smaller than the 3 preceding ones; suture moderate; mouth broad, oval, with a small wide sinus at the upper corner; 2 very strong and prominent parietal folds without any intervening ones; 3 or 4

81

82

plaits (folds) deep inside the outer lip, visible through the wall of the shell; peristome continuous, reflected, with a very strong white lip; umbilicus cleft, narrow; clausilium oblong, with a deep notch at the basal margin; surface almost smooth, glossy, with delicate transverse striations (lens!); colour yellow-brown tinged with red on the larger whorls, or greenish-white. H: 14–18 mm., B: 4 mm., W: 10–12. Animal spends day between ash or beech roots in woods, hedges, etc. (resembles fallen beech bud), and ascends trunks at night to feed on moss and lichens; lays a dozen eggs, each larger than the mouth of the shell. Distribution: frequent in England, sparse in N. and S. Wales, E. Scotland and Ireland; elsewhere Europe.

82. Rolph's Door Snail: *Clausilia (Plicaphora) rolphii* Turton. Shell sinistral, thin-walled, slightly translucent, club-shaped, broader in proportion than any other of our species, with the first 3 whorls forming a thick, stubby cylinder, increasing abruptly into the fourth; whorls convex; suture well marked; mouth larger and broader than in our other species, the lower half dilated and semicircular; 2 parietal folds, the lower less prominent, with 2 or 3 small folds in the space between; clausilium white, oblong, curved, narrowed above, not notched; surface glossy, with strong, close transverse striations, but no spiral striations (lens!); colour horn-brown to reddish-brown (lighter than other species), the ridges eroding to dirty grey. H: 12 mm., B: 3–3·5 mm., W: 9–11. Local in woodlands, scrub and hedges on calcareous soils. Distribution: S. and C. England north to Lincoln; elsewhere W. Europe.

83. Two-toothed Door Snail: *Clausilia* (*Clausilia*) *bidentata* (**Ström**). Shell sinistral, not thin, slightly translucent, club-shaped, the first three whorls forming a stubby cylinder; whorls slightly convex; body-whorl elongated, one-third the shell-height, narrower than the 2–3 preceding whorls; suture oblique, slight; mouth small, rounded, nearly funnel-shaped; 2 oblique parietal folds, the lower smaller and more sunken, with 1–3 smaller ribs between; a lunella and another slight tooth on the columellar lip; 1–2 folds within the outer lip; peristome continuous and lipped, columellar lip thickened and reflected; umbilicus narrow, cleft; clausilium oval-oblong, regularly curved, slightly expanded above, not notched; surface rather glossy, slightly granular through fine, criss-crossing cuticular spiral and transverse striations (lens!); light horn-colour, with white transverse streaks. H: 13 mm., B: 2·5 mm., W: 12–13. Common in woods, hedges, walls, gardens, etc. Distribution: British Isles; elsewhere W. and S. Europe.

84. Craven Door Snail: *Clausilia* (*C.*) *dubia* (**Draparnaud**). A larger version of *C. bidentata* and our largest *Clausilia* sp. Shell sinistral, club-shaped, more swollen than in *C. bidentata*; mouth pear-shaped, larger; peristome detached, rather reflected and feebly white-lipped; surface smoother, with a silky lustre, the penultimate whorl having 60–80 fine transverse ridges with fine striations between (lens!); horn-colour to blackish-brown, without white streaks. H: 11–16 mm., B: 3–3·5 mm., W: 10–12. Lives on rocks and walls, tree-trunks, etc., in hilly country. Distribution: N. England, Outer Hebrides; elsewhere Europe.

85. Two-lipped Door Snail: *Laciniaria biplicata* (**Montagu**). Shell sinistral, swollen club-shaped, the first three whorls forming a translucent cylinder, whereas the rest of the shell is opaque; whorls compressed; body-whorl less coiled and projecting somewhat; suture moderate; mouth pear-shaped, with a sinus at the upper corner and slightly jug-lipped at the lower extremity; upper parietal lip more prominent than lower, with 2 intervening folds; a slight tooth at the centre of the outer lip; peristome thick, white and reflected, forming a strong, continuous oval, the parietal lip detached; umbilicus shallow, broad; clausilium almost oval, strongly curved, narrow below, not notched; surface dull, with about 60 ribs on the penultimate whorl, these strong striations differing from those found in any other British species of the family (lens!); colour brown, pale horn-colour or grey, with the striations half-white. H: 16–19 mm., B: 4 mm., W: 12–13. Animal lives in hedges, banks, riversides (willow roots by day, trunks by night) and is very rare. Distribution: London area, Cambridge, Herts.; elsewhere Europe.

86. Tree Snail: *Balea perversa* (**L.**). Shell sinistral, club-shaped, without such a well-marked cylindrical apex as in other species of the family, and with the whorls increasing more regularly; whorls moderately convex; body-whorl rounded at the base; mouth a little more than semicircular, without folds or teeth, except for 1 small parietal tooth in some cases; peristome thin, pale, somewhat reflected; umbilicus minute; no clausilium; surface glossy, with irregular transverse striations; colour yellowish-brown. H: 8–9 mm., B: 2–2·5 mm., W: 6–8. Moss, lichens, crevices in rocks and trees; widespread, but local. Distribution: British Isles; elsewhere Europe west from Poland, Crimea, Atlantic Isles.

83

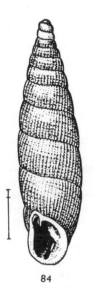

84

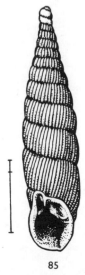

85

86

Family Ferussaciidae (*Spire Snails*)

A very small family of very small species, though, oddly enough, related to the giant tropical **Achatina achatina**, which, at 18 cm., is the world's largest land-snail. The shell is dextral, small, thin, glossy, more or less translucent, elongate-oval to conical, spire-shaped or nearly cylindrical, with a truncated apex; the whorls are weakly sculptured or smooth; the mouth is egg- or pear-shaped; the peristome is not expanded, but often thickened internally and sometimes toothed, and the columella (columellar lip) is notched or truncated. We have 1 species.

87. Blind Snail: *Cecilioides acicula* **(Müller).** Shell tiny, very thin-walled, transparent, slender, needle- or spire-shaped, with the greatest breadth in the lower part of the body-whorl; spire tapering very regularly with a truncated apex; whorls slightly convex; suture shallow; mouth narrow, pear-shaped, a little over one-third of the shell-height; peristome simple, centre of outer lip slightly inbowed, columella truncated; no umbilicus; surface smooth, glossy; colourless and clear in the fresh condition, becoming milky opaque. H: 4·5–5 mm., B: 1–1·3 mm., W: 5½–6½. Animal white, with unpigmented—therefore blind—eyes, in association with deep subterranean habit; only surfaces by accident (moles, rabbits, spades). Lives in calcareous soils on meadows, downs, graveyards; biology poorly known. Distribution: England, S. Wales, Denbigh, Anglesey, E., C. and S. Ireland; elsewhere W. and C. Europe, Atlantic Islands.

87

Slugs

On an earlier page in this book we observed that the popular term "snails" embraces several groups of animals which have considerable differences in structure and very varying degrees of relationship. The same applies to the expression "slugs", for, while anyone may believe that he understands very well what the word means to him, our British land-slugs include members of three different families of animals which have evolved independently from three different groups of snail ancestors. Thus, in treating these three families as one group in everyday speech and again now as a matter of practical convenience, we are adopting an artificial rather than a natural classification (see page 41).

Our three families are easily distinguished as follows:

1. Mantle at the posterior end of the body, protected by a small external shell . . . Family Testacellidae (Shelled Slugs).
2. Mantle at the anterior end of the body, forming a low mantle-shield and concealing an internal rudimentary plate-like or granular shell (Figure 23)

Figure 23

(a) Respiratory opening on the right side behind the middle of the mantle-shield . . . .
. . . . Family Limacidae (Keelback Slugs)

(b) Respiratory opening on the right side before the middle of the mantle-shield . . . .
. . . . Family Arionidae (Roundback Slugs)

(The respiratory opening is more easily distinguished when the animal is creeping and extended.)

SUPERFAMILY OLEACINACEA

Family Testacellidae (Shelled Slugs)

The ancestors of this family were jawless, carnivorous snails having reduced shells and acicular (needle-like) radular teeth, and belonging to a superfamily (Oleacinacea), unfortunately not otherwise represented in our fauna. In the Testacellid slugs the body broadens gradually posteriorly, and the heart, kidney, mantle-cavity and, of course, the mantle, are carried to the hinder end and protected by a small and rather absurd-looking auriform (ear-shaped) external shell. A pair of lateral grooves run from the front of the mantle to the head and give off several side-branches to the back and flanks. The posterior tentacles (eye-stalks) are not knobbed at the tips. There is no caudal mucus-gland. These slugs are subterranean by day and during winter hibernation. They are nocturnal carnivores, feeding to some extent on other slugs, centipedes, etc., but chiefly on earthworms, which they seize with their needle-like radular teeth, holding on grimly as their prey withdraws into its burrow. They are commonest on cultivated ground. We have 3 British species.

88. Maugé's Shelled Slug: *Testacella maugei* **Férussac.** Animal medium-sized, stocky, pear-shaped, with a prominent double row of tubercles along the back; origins of lateral grooves at front of mantle wide apart; groove-system forms conspicuous network; shell ear-shaped rectangular, convex, with hooked apex. Colour brown, paler at the sides, sprinkled with dark spots; sole yellow or pink; shell brown or white. Length of creeping animal extended to 60–100 mm.; shell 14 × 7 mm.; eggs 5 × 4 mm. Distribution: S., S.W., and W. England, Wales, S.W. Ireland; elsewhere Brittany, Portugal, S.W. Spain, Tangier, Atlantic Islands.

89. Shelled Slug: *Testacella haliotidea* **Draparnaud.** Animal medium-large, depressed, not so broad posteriorly as *T. maugei*, and with inconspicuous dorsal tubercles; origins of lateral grooves distinct, but close together; shell much smaller, rectangular, convex. Colour dull greyish-yellow; sole and foot-fringe pale; shell brown or white. Length of creeping animal extended to 80–120 mm.; shell 7 × 5 mm.; eggs 7 × 4 mm. Distribution: Great Britain north to Stirling, S.E. and S. Ireland; elsewhere Europe, N. Africa, Atlantic Islands. (*N.B.* Illustration shows slug contracted.)

90. Shield Shelled Slug: *Testacella scutulum* **Sowerby.** Animal medium-large, form and tubercles as *T. haliotidea*; origins of lateral grooves united; shell small, narrow, rectangular, flat or concave. Colour yellow sprinkled with brown; sole and foot-fringe brighter yellow; shell brown. Length of creeping animal extended to 80–120 mm.; shell 6 × 3·5 mm.; eggs 4 × 3 mm. Distribution: much as for *T. haliotidea*.

SUPERFAMILY ZONITACEA

Family Arionidae (*Roundback Slugs*)

These slugs are descended from snails close to the family Endodontidae (page 114) and classified with the latter in the superfamily Zonitacea. The mantle is restricted to the anterior part of the body and the respiratory pore opens well forward on its right margin. The North American **Binneya** retains an external spiral shell, but in our advanced British genera the mantle forms a granulose shield covering an internal shell, which is reduced to an oval plate in **Geomalacus** and to a mass of granules in **Arion**. The back is rounded and appears ridged and grooved through the presence of longitudinal rows of tubercles; the mid-dorsal row may be enlarged, but there is never such a keel as occurs in the Limacidae. The jaw is ribbed and the radular teeth are squarish, as in the Endodontidae. The foot has a fringe, wide in **Arion**, narrower in **Geomalacus**. The posterior tentacles (eye-stalks) have swollen tips. Our British species have a caudal mucus gland. Typically the animals live on the surface of the soil in most damp situations and are omnivorous. In the early stages of courtship the partners follow one another in a circle, each feeding on the mucus trail left by the other. We have 6 (or 7) British species.

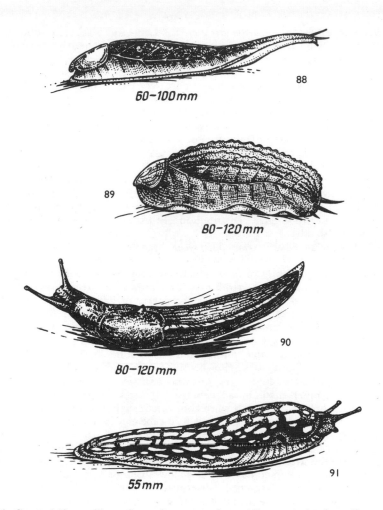

88

60–100 mm

89

80–120 mm

90

80–120 mm

91

55 mm

91. Spotted Kerry Slug: *Geomalacus maculosus* **Allman.** Animal medium-sized; skin glossy, with about 25 longitudinal rows of tiny polygonal tubercles. Adult grey, brown or black, with numerous irregular yellow or white spots (our only species with such a pattern); tentacles grey; foot brown, with fine dark stripes across narrow fringe; sole clear in the centre, with a yellow or grey band on either side. Length of creeping animal extended to 55 mm., esceptionally to 90 mm. Internal oval shell 4 × 3 mm. Animal can roll up like a woodlouse; lives and feeds on lichens, etc., on sandstone rocks and trees (camouflaged by coloration). Distribution: W. Cork, Kerry; elsewhere Brittany, N.W. Spain, Portugal (a Lusitanian distribution).

99

92. Large Black Slug: *Arion ater ater* (L.). **Large Red Slug:** *A. a. rufus* (L.). (Plate I), (two subspecies differing only in details of internal anatomy, but sometimes regarded as two separate species.) Animal large; skin tough, about 36 longitudinal rows of long coarse tubercles; mantle-shield coarsely granulose; fully opened respiratory pore very large. Animal can contract to a hemisphere. Adult all shades of brick-red (Plate I), brown or black (dozens of named colour-varieties), without markings; foot-fringe with alternating thick and thin transverse stripes which are broader at the hinder end; sole grey or yellow. Body-mucus very viscous, orange in red animals, otherwise colourless; sole-mucus always colourless. Length of creeping animal extended 150 mm., breadth 15–20 mm. Juvenile (to 40 mm.) yellow-white, greenish or grey-green, with dark tentacles. Ubiquitous and omnivorous; *A. a. rufus* appears to be more southerly and local on cultivated land, but records are still incomplete, owing to previous confusion with *A. a. ater*. Distribution: British Isles; elsewhere Europe, Atlantic Islands.

93. Lusitanian Slug: *Arion lusitanicus* **Mabille.** Animal medium-large; form, tubercles, contractility similar to *A. ater*, from which this species differs in the structure of the oviduct, and also in the smaller respiratory pore. Adult dark grey, reddish-yellow, brown or greenish-grey, with darker head and tentacles; foot-fringe darker or lighter, with transverse lines; sole pale or dark. Length of creeping animal extended 70–100 mm. Juvenile with dark lateral bands (cf. *A. fasciatus*, etc.), forming a lyre-shape on the mantle and surrounding the respiratory pore. Habits little known; confusion with *A. ater* probable. Distribution: Durham, Nuneaton, Berehaven on Bantry Bay; elsewhere Portugal, France, Switzerland.

94. Bourguignat's Slug: *Arion fasciatus* **(Nilsson).** (Formerly *A. circumscriptus*.) Animal small, broad, depressed, rather soft-skinned, with slender tubercles, bell-shaped in TS when contracted; slight keel of juvenile represented by median row of enlarged pale tubercles in adult; mantle-sheild finely granulose. Adult pale grey to slate grey; back darker, with median whitish keel-line; a dark lateral band on either side (higher up than in *A. hortensis* and arching *over* the respiratory pore), forming a lyre-shape on the mantle and sometimes with a yellow stripe below; foot-fringe pale, occasionally transverse-lined posteriorly; tentacles black; sole opaque white. Body- and sole-mucus colourless. Length of creeping animal extended 35–40 mm. Juvenile pale, with black head and tentacles. Ubiquitous under dead leaves, logs, etc., in woods, fields and gardens; nocturnal; slow-moving; feeds on fungi and rotting vegetation. Distribution: British Isles; elsewhere Europe.

95. Dusky Slug: *Arion subfuscus* **(Draparnaud).** Animal medium-sized, cylindrical, rather firm-skinned, with about 50 longitudinal rows of small slender tubercles; foot-fringe narrow; mantle-shield finely granulose. Animal cannot contract to a hemispherical shape. Adult ochre-yellow to coffee-brown, darker on the back, with a lyre-shaped mark on the mantle; respiratory pore pale-rimmed; foot-fringe pale, with dark transverse stripes; sole yellowish-white with white specks. Body-mucus yellow to

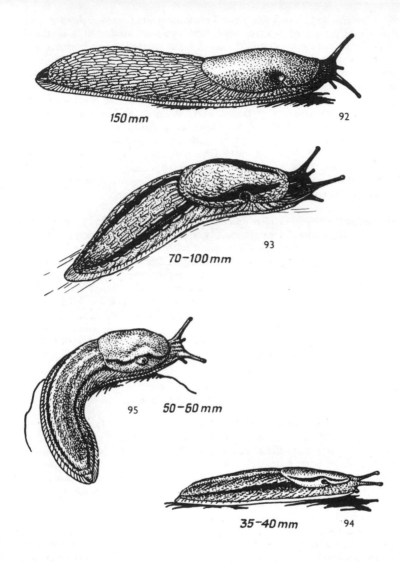

150 mm

92

70–100 mm

93

95   50–60 mm

35–40 mm   94

orange, sole-mucus colourless. Length of creeping animal extended 50–60 mm., rarely 70 mm. Juvenile grey with darker back, lateral bands and violet tentacles. Lives under logs, bark, etc., in deciduous and (unusual) coniferous woods, damp hedges, gardens, etc. Feeds on plants, fruit, fungi, carrion. Distribution: British Isles; elsewhere Europe, except Mediterranean region.

96. Garden Slug: *Arion hortensis* Férussac. Animal small, slender, cylindrical, rather narrow anteriorly, firm-skinned, about 48 longitudinal rows of broad tubercles (mid-dorsal row not enlarged); semicircular in TS when contracted. Adult dark brown-grey, peppered with yellow-brown dots; a blackish longitudinal band on either side (lower on the body than in *A. fasciatus* and surrounding the respiratory pore) is sharp-edged towards the back, but blurred into pale grey towards the foot; foot-fringe yellowish, occasionally with faint transverse lines; sole yellowish to orange. Body-mucus pale to dark yellow, sole-mucus colourless. Length of creeping animal extended 25–30 mm. Juvenile slate-grey, darker on the back, with lateral bands, no keel and violet-brown tentacles. Common in gardens, parks and fields (one of the few serious pest species), also in woods under logs, etc. Burrows in the soil and feeds on the underground and lower parts of plants. Distribution: British Isles; elsewhere Europe.

97. Hedgehog Slug: *Arion intermedius* Normand. Animal very small, stocky, with the back sloping steeply towards the hinder end; in the contracted state the tubercles are conical with translucent tips. Adult pale yellowish-grey, darker on the back; head darker; lateral bands present or absent, in the former case arching over the respiratory pore and sending a posterior branch beneath it; mid-dorsal row of tubercles yellowish-white; foot-fringe yellowish-grey; sole yellow-white. Mucus golden yellow, accumulating at both ends of the animal. Length of creeping animal extended 15–20 mm., rarely 25 mm. Juvenile similar to adult. Common under moist rubbish in woods and fields; eats fungi. Distribution: British Isles; elsewhere Europe, Azores.

Family Limacidae (*Keelback Slugs*)

These slugs are descended from snails close to the family Vitrinidae (page 114), and classified with the later in the superfamily Zonitacea. The mantle is restricted to the anterior part of the body and forms a granulose or concentrically ringed shield concealing a flat oval shell. The respiratory pore opens on the right edge of the mantle-shield, behind its centre. The body is covered with many longitudinal rows of skin-tubercles. The jaw is arcuate (arched) with a lower median projection, the marginal teeth of the radula are pointed, there is a groove around the base of the foot and no caudal mucus-gland; these 4 characters are shared with the Vitrinidae. The back is keeled more or less up to the mantle-shield. The sole is tripartite, i.e. longitudinally divided into a median region with chevron-like grooves and 2 lateral regions, which are easily seen when the slug is made to crawl on a piece of glass. The posterior tentacles (eye-stalks) have swollen tips. Nocturnal animals, concealed by day but usually living on the surface of the soil in damp places. Some are pests and some have specialised habits, but generally these slugs are omnivorous upon almost anything but green plants. We have 13 British species.

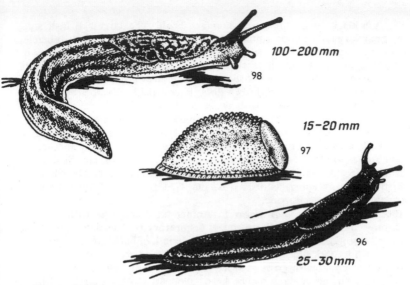

100-200 mm
98

15-20 mm
97

96
25-30 mm

Key to British genera:

1. Mantle-shield granulose, with a horseshoe-shaped furrow; back keeled right up to
the hinder edge of the mantle (subfamily *Parmacellinae*)................*Milax*
Mantle-shield concentrically ridged, without a horseshoe-shaped furrow; back
rarely keeled as far as mantle (subfamily *Limacinae*).................. 2

2. Body full of water, gelatinous, translucent......................*Lehmannia*
Body firmer, more or less opaque.................................... 3

3. Nucleus of concentric mantle-ridges lies to the right of the mid-dorsal line, over
the respiratory pore; tail obliquely truncate (i.e. the tip slopes suddenly and
steeply)..*Agriolimax* (=*Deroceras*)
Nucleus of concentric mantle-ridges lies on the mid-dorsal line; back slopes gently
all the way to the end of the pointed tail...........................*Limax*

98. Great Grey Slug: *Limax maximus* L. (Plate II.) Animal large, with
about 48 longitudinal rows of long elliptical tubercles, whose points
interdigitate at either end; the mantle-shield, rounded and free anteriorly,
pointed posteriorly, occupies about one-third of the body-length; the
posterior one-third of the back is keeled. Adult pale grey to whitish, grey-
brown or dark grey, but never black; mantle-shield dark-spotted or
marbled; 2–3 dark longitudinal bands or rows of spots on either side
(rarely absent); keel pale; tentacles pale pinkish-brown, without spots; sole
uniformly pale; mucus colourless. Length of creeping animal extended
100–200 mm. Shell 11 × 7 mm. Juvenile pale grey with inner lateral bands
and pale pinkish-grey tentacles. Species lives mainly near man in gardens,
parks, cellars and yards, also under logs, bark and stones in woods; feeds
on fungi and decaying matter; after a circling courtship, mates suspended
from thick thread of mucus in mid-air. Eggs 5 × 5·5 mm., soft, amber-
coloured. Distribution: British Isles; elsewhere Europe, Asia Minor,
N. Africa, Atlantic Islands.

99. Ash-black Slug: *Limax cinereoniger* **Wolf.** The largest British slug. Animal very large; body similar to *L. maximus*, but with coarser tubercles and the posterior half of the back keeled. Adult usually uniform grey or black, with a dark mantle-shield and white keel-line, less often with dark longitudinal stripes or rows of spots on a pale-grey ground; tentacles dark, with minute black or dark brown dots; lateral fields of sole grey-black to black, sharply contrasted with white median field. Length of creeping animal extended 100–200 mm., exceptionally to 400 mm. (Ellis). Shell 9 × 5 mm. Juvenile translucent white, becoming opaque brown and then black. The country cousin of *L. maximus*; lives under rotten wood, leaves and stones in woods and open country, never in gardens, etc. Mates suspended from a pad of mucus after a circling courtship. Distribution: British Isles, except parts of East Anglia, C. England, S. Scotland and C. Ireland; elsewhere Europe.

100. Yellow Slug: *Limax flavus* **L.** Animal medium-large with a rather stumpy "tail" and smooth tubercles; respiratory pore encircled by a pale elevated ring; keel blunt, less than half the length of back. Adult apparently yellowish to dark orange or greenish, suffused with grey or dusky; mantle-shield dark yellowish-green, spotted or mottled with yellow; yellow spots on body, but never dark bands; head greenish; tentacles cold steel-blue; sole uniformly pale yellow; mucus yellow, which accounts for much of apparent colour of basically grey animal. Length of creeping animal extended 70–100 mm. Shell 9 × 6 mm. Juvenile pale greenish-yellow, with blue tentacles. Common in gardens, wall-crevices, cellars and larders (very secretive by day), also under logs, etc., in woods; feeds on fungi, decayed plants, garbage; mates on ground; eggs 6 × 4 mm., pale amber, lemon-shaped (nubs). Distribution: British Isles; elsewhere Europe, Asia Minor, N. Africa.

101. Slender or Tender Slug: *Limax tenellus* **Müller.** Our smallest *Limax* species. Animal small, delicate, gelatinous, waxy; hinder end of back feebly keeled. Adult pale yellow, with an orange mantle-shield and sometimes with more or less faint mantle- and lateral bands; head and tentacles black or dark brown; sole pale; mucus yellow or orange. Length of creeping animal extended 25–35 mm. Shell 3·5 × 2 mm. Juvenile translucent white, with pale violet tentacles. (*N.B.:* cf. *Lehmannia marginata*, page 106.) Widespread, but very local on fungi in old woods, including (unusual) pinewoods. Mates on ground after circling courtship. Distribution: Great Britain; elsewhere Europe, Asia Minor, N. Africa.

102. Netted Slug: *Agriolimax reticulatus* **Müller.** Our commonest slug, formerly generally confused with the much rarer *A. agrestis*. Animal small; mantle-shield rounded at both ends, more than one-third of the body-length; a raised white ring around the respiratory pore; back with a short keel; tail obliquely truncate. Adult very variable: whitish, cream or brownish-yellow to blue-black with a network or mottled pattern of dark brown grooves, spots and streaks; tentacles dark; sole yellowish-white; mucus milky-white (lime), sticky. Length of creeping animal extended to 35 mm. Shell oblong-oval, 5 × 3 mm. Juvenile translucent pale grey. Ubiquitous in hordes, omnivorous and a very serious crop pest; mates on

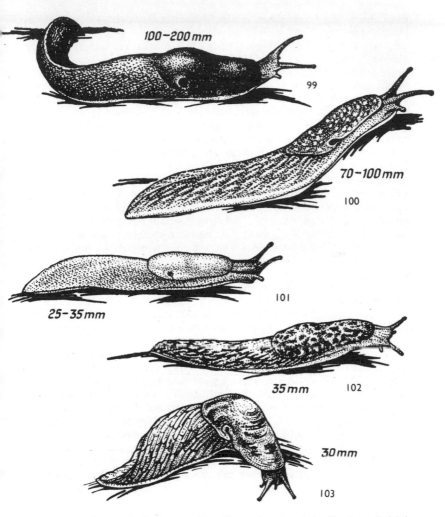

the ground after a circling courtship; lives one year. Distribution: British Isles; elsewhere Europe, N. Africa, Atlantic Islands.

103. Field Slug: *Agriolimax agrestis* (L.). Animal small; smaller, smoother and slenderer than *A. reticulatus*, with which it has been widely confused. Adult pale greyish-yellow, paler on the sides, sometimes with whitish and/ or a few dark spots; in general less pigmented than the above. Length of creeping animal extended 30 mm. Shell angular, 3·5 × 2 mm. Juvenile translucent, whitish, without bands. Prefers wetter sites than the above and in this country is very local in fen carr (i.e. waterlogged fen woodland). Distribution: Norfolk; elsewhere Europe.

104. Marsh Slug: *Agriolimax laevis* (Müller). Animal very small, smooth, glossy, translucent and active; mantle-shield placed nearer the middle of the body and with fewer ridges than in other species; respiratory pore less obviously ringed; back slightly keeled. Adult light or dark brown, sometimes reddish or greenish, with dark spots; mantle-shield paler; tentacles black; sole pale brown; mucus colourless, watery. Length of creeping animal extended 17–25 mm. Shell oblong-oval, 3×1.5 mm. Juvenile translucent white with violet-tinged light pinkish-brown tentacles. Ubiquitous on marshes, river banks, meadows, etc., and sometimes on drier sites; has been known to eat insects (mealy bugs, *Coccus* sp.); mates on the ground without a circling prelude. Distribution: British Isles; elsewhere Europe, N. Asia, N. America.

105. Caruana's Slug: *Agriolimax caruanae* Pollonera. Animal small, similar in form to *A. laevis*, but larger, still more active and irritable. Adult dark, translucent chestnut, grey-brown or grey with a lighter mantle-shield, all flecked with dark brown; a pale ring round the respiratory pore; sole grey; mucus colourless, watery. Length of creeping animal extended 25–30 mm. Shell rectangular, 4.5×2 mm. Lives mainly in gardens, etc., also in fields, hedges and waste places; fast, aggressive and cannibalistic; mates on the ground after a circling courtship and tail-licking. Distribution: local in Great Britain and S. Ireland; elsewhere Malta, Marseilles, Canary Islands.

106. Tree Slug: *Lehmannia marginata* (Müller). Animal medium-sized, very soft, gelatinous and translucent under damp conditions, owing to the high water-content of the body; tubercles smooth; mantle-shield rounded and fixed anteriorly, bluntly pointed posteriorly; back sloping gradually to the tip of the tail, the hinder part keeled. Adult grey, usually darker in the centre of the mantle-shield, with a lighter median stripe down the back; 2 more or less distinct dark longitudinal bands on each flank, the inner ones generally darker and forming a lyre-pattern on the mantle; head and tentacles little pigmented, but the dark retractor muscles show through the skin; sole pale to white; mucus colourless, watery, exuded in great quantities when the animal is irritated. Length of creeping animal extended to over 75 mm. Shell 4×2.7 mm. (*N.B.:* Cf. *Limax tenellus* in the case of small dry-weather specimens.) Juvenile pale, translucent grey, with a conspicuous lyre-pattern and violet tentacles. Lives in woods, climbs tree-trunks in wet weather and feeds on fungi and lichens; can descend by a mucus-thread and ascend again; mates on flat, vertical or overhanging surfaces. Distribution: British Isles; elsewhere Europe.

107. Smooth Jet Slug: *Milax gagates* (Draparnaud). Animal rather small, smooth, having longitudinal rows of flattened tubercles with unpigmented grooves between these; the centre of the granulose mantle-shield is demarcated by a horseshoe-shaped furrow, open posteriorly (generic character); the dorsal keel is abruptly truncated at the posterior end. Adult uniform grey or black, lighter towards the foot, but with a darker keel; no lateral bands (generic character); respiratory pore not pale-ringed; sole pale; mucus colourless and sticky. Length of creeping animal extended 50 mm. Shell elliptical, 4×2.5 mm. Life-history poorly known. Generally distributed in gardens, wild places and on cliffs, especially near the sea; a root-crop pest. Distribution: England, Wales, S. Scotland, Ireland; elsewhere N.W. Europe, S. France.

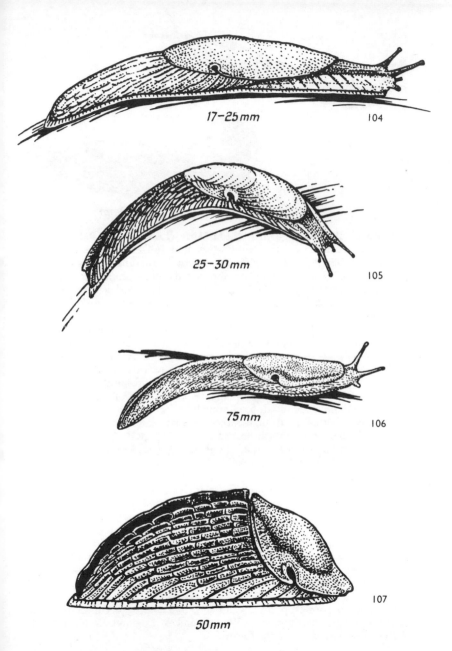

17-25 mm   104

25-30 mm   105

75 mm   106

107

50 mm

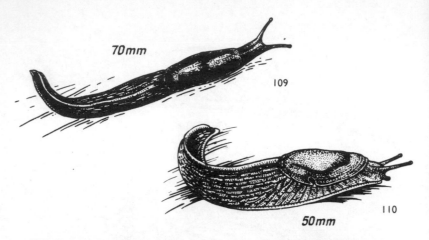

70mm

109

50mm

110

108. Rough Jet Slug: *Milax* cf. *insularis* **(Lessona and Pollonera).** A "problem species" whose identification and full characterisation await further research. Apart from details of internal structure, it differs from *M. gagates* in being larger, rougher (through its more prominent tubercles) and having more intense black pigmentation and a darker sole. Distribution: Bexhill, Sussex; elsewhere Mediterranean Europe.

109. Sowerby's Slug, Keeled Slug: *Milax sowerbyi* **(Férussac).** Animal medium-sized, less compressed than *M. gagates* and rather dry; body with about 14–19 pigmented grooves on each side, joined by transverse grooves; keel prominent, but not abruptly truncated posteriorly. Adult pale to dark brown or grey, with darker specks; keel paler; respiratory pore pale-ringed; sole pale; mucus yellow and sticky. Length of creeping animal extended 70 mm. Shell oval, 5 × 3 mm. Juvenile speckled with black, with a pale keel. Common, though rather subterranean in habit, in gardens, cultivated land and rubbish-heaps; a root-crop pest. Mating follows a circling courtship. Distribution: England, Wales, S. Scotland, Ireland; elsewhere Mediterranean Europe.

110. Budapest Slug: *Milax budapestensis* **(Hazay).** Our smallest *Milax* sp. Animal small, slender; body covered with longitudinal rows of polygonal tubercles, with pigmented grooves between; back keeled. Forms a semi-circle in the contracted state (other species form a compressed helmet shape). Animal black or brownish, mantle paler; keel dirty yellow or orange; respiratory pore grey-ringed; edge of foot and sole dark; lateral fields of sole grey, median field dark grey to black; mucus colourless and sticky. Length of creeping animal extended 50 mm. Shell elliptical, brown, 3 × 1·25 mm. Juvenile pale yellowish-grey. Lives mainly on cultivated land; a root-crop pest. Courtship and mating occur under loose stones and logs. Distribution: S.W., S.E. and W. England, E., N. and S.W. Wales, S. Ireland; elsewhere Europe.

Family *Zonitidae* (*Glass Snails*)

Land-snails with a smooth, thin, dextral, conical or flattened shell. The marginal teeth of the radula are pointed; the jaw is arcuate, not ribbed, with a central keel ending in a projection on the lower edge; there is a pedal groove around the edge of the foot and a mucus gland at the hinder end of it. The Zonitidae hide themselves in damp places under dead leaves, stones, etc., by day and come out at night; some species have carnivorous habits, attacking earthworms, etc. We have 12 British species. It is hardly possible to define the genera on shell-characters alone, but the following key may help:

1. Shell conical, top-shaped.................................*Euconulus*
   Shell depressed 2

2. Umbilicus tiny; shell glassy, whitish or greenish......................*Vitrea*
   Umbilicus wide; shell horny... 3

3. Mouth as broad as tall; adult shell-breadth 6–8 mm.; dart-sac present.........
   ....*Zonitoides*
   Mouth obviously broader than tall; no dart-sac........................ 4

4. Adult shell-breadth 4–5·5 mm.; whorls 4½–5.......................*Retinella*
   Adult shell-breadth 6·5–12 mm.; whorls 4½–6....................*Oxychilus*

111. Crystal Snail: *Vitrea crystallina* (**Müller**). Shell very small, thin-walled, transparent, stocky discoidal, more convex below than above, with a slightly elevated spire; body-whorl rounded beneath, less than twice as broad as previous one at mouth; mouth crescentic, regularly arched on columellar side; peristome strengthened by a weak white lip; umbilicus very narrow, slightly eccentric, funnel-shaped; surface glossy, with very fine transverse striations (lens!); colourless or with a faint greenish tinge. H: 1·65 mm., B: 2·8–3·2 mm., W: 4¾. Animal greyish-white, white spots on mantle, black posterior tentacles. General in damp sites under leaves, stones, etc., in marshes, meadows, woods and hedges. Distribution: British Isles; elsewhere Europe to Central Russia, Atlantic Islands.

111

109

112. Milky Crystal Snail: *Vitrea contracta* (Westerlund). Shell still smaller, feebly translucent, discoidal, flatter, with a lower spire; whorls more closely coiled; body-whorl flattened beneath, less than twice as broad as the previous one at the mouth; mouth crescentic, arch slightly hooked on columellar side; peristome without white lip; umbilicus funnel-shaped, forming a regular spiral; colour milk-white to yellowish. H: 1·25 mm., B: 2·3–2·5 mm., W: 4½. Lives in humus under dead leaves. Distribution: British Isles (largely replaces *V. crystallina* in Ireland); elsewhere Europe.

113. Rayed Glass Snail: *Retinella (Perpolita) radiatula* (Alder). Shell very small, thin-walled, transparent, biconvex with a very low conical spire; body-whorl twice as broad as previous one at the mouth; mouth elliptical-crescentic, cut by last whorl; peristome strengthened by weak lip; umbilicus funnel-shaped, wider by the end of the last whorl; surface glossy, with deep radiating striations continuous across whorls; colour reddish horn-brown, rarely greenish. H: 2–2·2 mm., B: 3·5–4·3 mm., W: 3½–4½. Animal grey with grey mantle and blue-black head and back. Nearly ubiquitous in damp sites in marshes, meadows, woods, etc. Distribution: British Isles; elsewhere Holarctic (i.e. Europe, N. Asia and N. America).

114. Clear Glass Snail: *Retinella (Aegopinella) pura* (Alder). Shell very small, thin-walled, nearly transparent, more convex below than above, with a slightly elevated spire; body-whorl dilated towards mouth; mouth elliptical-crescentic, cut by last whorl; umbilicus wide, diameter almost one-fourth of shell-breadth; upperside silky, underside more glossy, finely cross-striated (lens!); pale reddish-horn colour to white. H: 2–2·6 mm., B: 4–4·6 mm., W: 3¾–4¼. Animal white to pale yellow, mantle white spotted with black, back grey. General under moist dead leaves and moss, in woods and shady places. Distribution: British Isles; elsewhere Europe.

115. Smooth Glass Snail: *Retinella (Aegopinella) nitidula* (Draparnaud). Shell small, rather strong-walled, slightly translucent, with a slightly raised conical spire; the body-whorl does not increase perceptibly towards the mouth, where it is from one and three-quarters times to twice as broad as the previous whorl; mouth almost as tall as broad; umbilicus wide and deep; surface rather dull with distinct cross-striations (lens!); colour reddish-amber above, paler below. H: 5–5·5 mm., B: 8–9 mm., W: 4½–5. Animal grey to black. Under leaves and stones in woods, hedges, etc. Distribution: British Isles; elsewhere Europe.

116. Draparnaud's Glass Snail: *Oxychilus draparnaldi* (Beck). Our largest species. Shell medium-sized, thick-walled, translucent, with a slightly raised conical spire; the body-whorl is slightly dilated at the mouth where it is twice as broad as the previous whorl; mouth elongate-elliptical, cut by last whorl; umbilicus diameter about one-eighth breadth of shell; surface glossy with irregular striations (lens); pale to dark horn-colour, lighter underneath. H: 6–7 mm., B: 12–14 mm., W: 5¾–6. Animal deep grey-blue, with grey mantle. Lives among dead leaves, under stones, etc., and is carnivorous (earthworms). Distribution: Great Britain (except Midlands) north to Aberdeen, Ireland; elsewhere S. and W. Europe, N.W. Africa, Madeira.

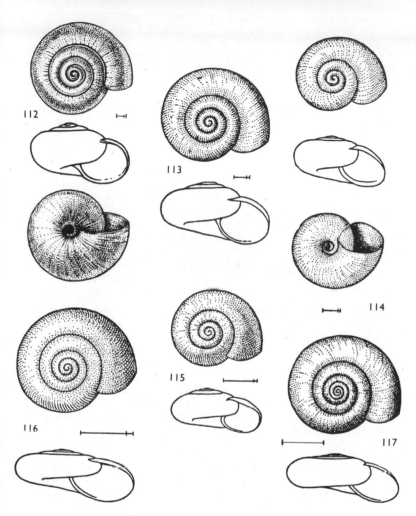

112 113 114 115 116 117

117. Cellar Glass Snail: *Oxychilus cellarius* (**Müller**). Shell small, thin-walled, translucent, discoidal with a very depressed spire; whorls increase slowly and regularly; body-whorl twice breadth of previous one at mouth; mouth elliptical, broader and less oblique than previous species; columellar lip slightly reflected; umbilicus funnel-shaped, diameter from one-sixth to one-seventh of shell-breadth; surface glossy, feebly and indistinctly striated (lens); colour yellowish-grey, underside white. H: 5–5·5 mm., B: 10–11 mm., W: $5\frac{1}{2}$–$5\frac{3}{4}$. Animal slate-grey, darker above, with edge of mantle spotted with brown; has unpleasant smell. Carnivore and fungus-eater. Nearly ubiquitous in damp, shady sites in woods, gardens, back-yards and cellars. Distribution: British Isles; elsewhere Central Europe, W. Mediterranean Region, Algeria, Atlantic Islands.

111

118. Garlic Glass Snail: *Oxychilus alliarius* **(Miller).** Shell small, translucent, convex above, flattened below, with a slightly elevated spire; body-whorl twice diameter of previous whorl at mouth; mouth oblique, broadly elliptical, cut by last whorl; umbilicus funnel-shaped, one-sixth of shell-breadth; surface glossy, with regular weak striations (lens!); horn-coloured, paler below. H: 2·5 mm., B: 6·5 mm., W: 4–4½. Animal blue-black; smells strongly of garlic (*Allium*; hence name) when irritated. Nearly ubiquitous in woods, fields, gardens, etc. Distribution: British Isles; elsewhere N. Europe to France.

119. Glossy Glass Snail: *Oxychilus helveticus* **(Blum).** Shell small, transparent, convex above, flatter below, with a slightly elevated spire; body-whorl twice breadth of previous whorl at mouth; mouth elliptical-crescentic, cut by last whorl; peristome simple; umbilicus small and deep; surface smooth, glossy, with very faint striations (lens!); colour pale brown, whitish underneath. H: 5–5·5 mm., B: 9–10 mm., W: 5. Animal blue-grey, with darker cross-stripes and a black edge to the mantle. Lives in moist sites in woods, hedges, etc. Distribution: Great Britain north to Banff, sparse in Scotland; elsewhere France, Belgium, Switzerland.

120. Shiny Glass Snail: *Zonitoides nitidus* **(Müller).** Shell small, rather transparent, depressed globular, convex above, flatter below, with a slightly elevated conical spire; whorls increase regularly; body-whorl rather swollen, twice breadth of previous whorl at mouth; mouth obliquely inclined, broadly elliptical-crescentic, cut by last whorl; umbilicus wide, funnel-shaped, diameter from one-fifth to one-fourth of shell-breadth; surface glossy, finely striated (lens!); colour red-brown. H: 4 mm., B: 8 mm., W: 4½–4¾. Animal deep blue-black, mantle grey with black spots. Common on marshes, river banks and wet places. Distribution: British Isles north to Outer Hebrides; elsewhere Holarctic.

121. Hollowed Glass Snail: *Zonitoides excavatus* (*Alder*). Shell transparent, depressed globular, convex above and below, with a slightly elevated spire; whorls increase regularly; body-whorl rather swollen, twice breadth of previous whorl at mouth; mouth small, round, cut by last whorl; umbilicus broader and very deep; surface glossy with strong irregular striations; horn-coloured, paler below. H: 3 mm., B: 6–7 mm., W: 5½–6. Animal greyish, mantle spotted with white. Local in woods on non-calcareous soils. Distribution: British Isles north to Outer Hebrides, but absent from much of E. and C. England, E. and N. Scotland, N.E. and C. Ireland; elsewhere N. Belgium, Holland and N.W. Germany.

122. Tawny Glass Snail: *Euconulus fulvus* **(Müller).** Shell very small, thin-walled, translucent, globose, with a well-elevated conical spire; whorls increase gradually; body-whorl has a blunt peripheral keel; mouth crescentic; no umbilicus; surface glossier below than above, with fine irregular striations (lens!); colour reddish-brown. H: 2–2·3 mm., B: 2·5–3 mm., W: 5–6. Animal grey-black. Lives in woods, marshes, etc. Distribution: British Isles; elsewhere Holarctic.

Plate III. Typical Snails (Family Helicidae), all about $1\frac{1}{3}$-$1\frac{1}{2}$ times life-size. *Above left:* White-lipped Snail, *Cepaea hortensis* (Müller), band-variety 1(23)45 (*see* p. 132). *Below left:* Copse Snail, *Arianta arbustorum* (L.) (*see* p. 120). *Right:* Two varieties of the Brown-lipped Snail, *C. nemoralis* (L.) (*see* p. 130). *Above:* Bandless form 00000. *Below:* Band-variety ::3::. Note also the variations in colour and in the elevation of the spire. (Photos by Dr. Helmut Länge.)

Plate IV. Roman Snail, *Helix pomatia* L., about 1½ times life-size. In Britain this species spends about half the year in hibernation; as winter approaches it burrows under dead leaves and sometimes a few centimetres into the underlying soil, turns the mouth of its shell upwards and then closes it with a thick epiphragm composed of hardened mucus-secretion heavily impregnated with lime salts. Within this it secretes a second epiphragm of hardened mucus only. The pore shown in the epiphragm in the upper photo is frequent in other species but unusual in *H. pomatia* whose epiphragm is porous enough to breathe through and normally lacks an opening. *Below:* Awakening after a warm spring shower, the Roman Snail heaves the epiphragm open with its foot like a trap-door. The epiphragm then usually falls clear and is discarded, but sometimes a few remnants of it remain clinging to the mouth of the shell. (Photos by Richard Kern.)

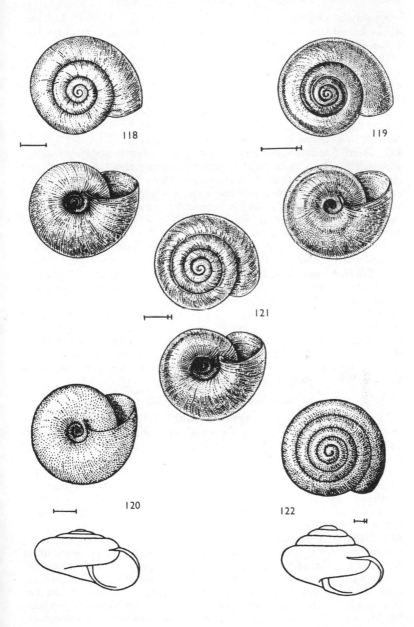

118

119

121

120

122

Family Endodontidae (*Discus Snails*)

An old and widespread family of primitive land-snails, having a flattened, round dextral shell, a thin, non-reflected peristome (often without thickening), a wide and deep umbilicus and square teeth on the radula. They are liable to be confused with the Pyramidulidae (higher spire, stepped whorls), Valloniidae (thickened, reflected peristome) and Zonitidae (larger body-whorl and frequently greater size). *Punctum* is very tiny (B: 1·6 mm.), and has a remarkable jaw, which almost surrounds the mouth and is composed of 19 separate plates, which fuse with age. *Discus* is larger (B: 7·5 mm.) and has the jaw in one piece. The Endodontidae are close to the ancestors of the Arionid slugs (page 98). We have 2 British species.

123. Dwarf Snail: *Punctum pygmaeum* (Draparnaud). Shell thin-walled, minute, almost discoidal, with a smooth, scarcely elevated spire; whorls cylindrical, increasing gradually; mouth nearly round, oblique, circle broken by previous whorl; peristome sharp, simple; umbilicus broad and very deep; surface with a silky lustre and fine, close rib-striations (lens!); pale to dark horn-colour. H: 0·6–0·9 mm., B: 1·2–1·6 mm., W: 3½. Animal grey-brown, with black dots. Common among dead leaves, under stones, etc., in woods, hedges and marshes. Distribution: British Isles; elsewhere Europe and N. Asia (i.e. Palaearctic).

124. Rounded Snail: *Discus rotundatus* (Müller). Shell small, lens-shaped, with a very slightly elevated spire; whorls cylindrical, increasing gradually, the last with a blunt peripheral keel; mouth as above; peristome thin, simple, with internal rib; umbilicus wide (greatest diameter one-third of breadth); surface strongly ribbed (especially on spire side) and finely striated (lens!); colour yellow-brown, with curved radial red-brown flecks. H: 2·4–3 mm., B: 6–7·5 mm., W: 6–7. Common among dead leaves, under stones, bark, rotten wood, etc. Distribution: British Isles; elsewhere Europe, N.W. Africa, Atlantic Islands.

Family Vitrinidae (*Glass Snails*)

Land-snails which are nearly related to the Zonitidae, and resemble the latter in the structure of the radula and jaw and in a tendency towards carnivorous habits. Here, however, the dextral shell has fewer whorls and is more globose, larger-mouthed and much more delicate and, in life, is partly invested anteriorly and to the right by reflexed folds of the mantle. The long foot lacks a posterior mucus gland. The animals inhabit damp and cool places and conceal themselves in summer. The Vitrinidae stand very close to the ancestors of the Limacidae, one of our 3 British families of terrestrial slugs. We have 3 British species.

125. Pellucid Glass Snail: *Vitrina* (*V.*) *pellucida* (Müller). Shell small, very thin-walled, transparent, globose-depressed, with a very low, blunt, conical spire; the whorls increase rapidly but regularly; the body-whorl is large, but not distended towards the mouth; mouth large, flattened circular, half the shell-breadth; peristome sharp; no umbilicus; surface almost smooth, glossy; colour yellowish-green. H: 3–3·4 mm., B: 4–6 mm., W: 3½. Animal grey, with a black head; carnivorous (earthworms) and

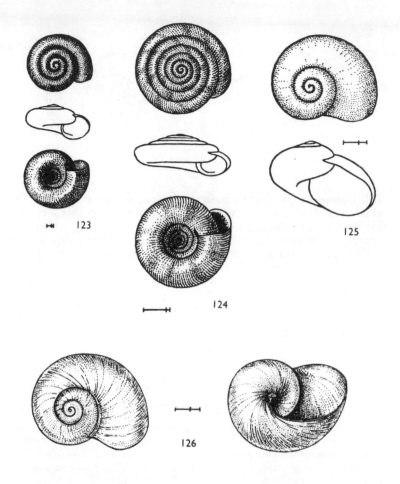

123

125

124

126

coprophagous (horse-dung); common under leaves, moss, stones, logs in damp woods. Distribution: British Isles; elsewhere Europe, N. and C. Asia, Algeria.

126. Greater Pellucid Glass Snail: *Vitrina* (*Phenacolimax*) *major* (Férussac). Shell almost indistinguishable from above, except for broader mouth, flatter spire and sometimes sharper columellar lip. The animal, however, is black (grey with a black head in *V. pellucida*), larger in proportion to its shell, has more generous mantle-folds, and crawls with "unusual vivacity". Rare and local in old woodlands. Distribution: Devon, Somerset, Bucks., Gloucester, Hereford, Monmouth, Brecon; elsewhere W. Germany to Catalonia and Italy.

127

127. Pyrenean Glass Snail: *Vitrina (Semilimax) pyrenaica* (**Férussac**). Shell small, very thin-walled, translucent, flat and compressed, with a flat spire like the marine Ormer (*Haliotis*); the whorls increase rapidly and the body-whorl forms most of the shell; mouth oval, very oblique, two-thirds of the shell-breadth; peristome sharp, with a membranous fringe on the lower margin; no umbilicus; surface smooth with faint striations (lens!), very glossy; colour yellowish-green. H: 2 mm., B: 5 mm., W: $2\frac{1}{2}$. Animal pale translucent grey, mantle similar with large black spots. The mantle is so voluminous that it extends over the spire. Local under leaves, etc., in damp woods; probably introduced. Distribution: Ireland, near Collon, Monasterboice and Mellifont Abbey, Louth and Meath; elsewhere Pyrenees.

SUPERFAMILY HELICACEA

Family Helicidae (Typical Snails)

The large number (26) of our British land-snails belonging to the Family Helicidae is a fair reflection of the fact that this is a very successful family containing more species than any other in the whole Phylum Mollusca. It also provides a promise and explanation of the difficulty we shall have in defining and identifying them, for the Helicidae, having, as it were, found that a relatively primitive and generalised ground-plan proved to be a very practical, adaptable and flexible one, have greatly diversified their habits and habitats and developed a great many secondary modifications in association with these. As a consequence, the natural classification of the family depends on the appreciation of details of internal anatomy which are largely beyond the scope of this book, while the shell, such a reliable guide in most of the families previously dealt with, now becomes a very plastic and variable structure, varying greatly in relation to mode of life and often showing such parallel or convergent similarities between different genera as to become very misleading indeed. This is well illustrated in the key below, where it will be seen that a practical classification based entirely on shell-characters often cuts right across the divisions of the natural classification based on internal anatomy.

116

In general, the Helicidae have a more or less globose, dextral shell with a relatively large body-whorl and a medium-sized spire (as in our common species of **Helix** and **Cepaea**), but in some cases the shell is elongate (**Cochlicella**) and in many it is depressed and even discoidal. In some species of **Hygromia** and **Monacha** the shell is covered with fine hairs, outgrowths from the periostracum. There is a greater range of colouring than in most of the previous families, and pigmented patterns, usually based on a system of spiral bands, are frequent. The animal lacks a pedal groove around the edge of the foot; the jaw is arched and transversely ridged, often folded, but without projections; the radula has square teeth; the male and female ducts open by a common genital pore below the right posterior tentacle; a dart-sac, secreting a calcareous love-dart (pages 19, 164), is usually present and there is a more or less complicated system of mucus glands opening into the vagina (Figure 5).

The Helicidae occur in most terrestrial habitats, surviving drought or cold by summer aestivation or winter hibernation, during which they frequently seal the mouths of their shells by a false operculum or epiphragm (Plate IV), formed from a series of membranes of hardened mucus. Courtship behaviour is often protracted and elaborate, and the eggs are buried deep in the soil. As a rule these snails are herbivorous and gregarious, emerging in troops after a shower, and often "homing" to an individual or communal roosting-place when conditions become drier.

KEY TO THE BRITISH SPECIES OF HELICIDAE

1. Shell elongate (height more than twice the breadth).........*Cochlicella acuta*
   Shell not elongate.. 2

2. Shell perfectly conical, with a flattened base; H: 6 mm., B: 7·5 mm.; found near Dover (Kent) or Chaldon (Surrey)......................*Helicella elegans*
   Shell other than perfectly conical.................................... 3

3. Shell very depressed (breadth more than 2·3 times the height)............. 4
   Shell depressed (breadth 1·5 to 2·0 times the height).................... 5
   Shell globose-depressed (breadth 1·25 to 1·5 times the height)............ 15
   Shell globose or subglobose (breadth less than 1·25 times the height)....... 22

   N.B.: Borderline cases are provided for by duplication in the key,
   but in case of doubt test the next possible category.

4. Shell lens-shaped, with an elevated spire and sharp peripheral keel; not hairy; peristome continuous, white-lipped and detached from parietal wall; brown with red-brown patches............................*Helicigona lapicida*
   Shell thick disc-shaped, with a flat or partly sunken spire; hairy or pitted by the microscopic scars of fallen hairs; peristome interrupted, red- or purple-lipped; brownish...*Helicodonta obvoluta*

5. Shell-breadth 1·9 to 2·1 times the height; spire only slightly elevated; never hairy; umbilicus broad; white or creamy with several dark spiral bands which are faint or absent above the periphery....................................... 6
   Shell-breadth less than 1·9 times the height............................ 7

6. Umbilicus central; no bands above the periphery..............*Helicella itala*
   Umbilicus eccentric; faint bands above the periphery..............*H. gigaxi*

7. Shell with pigmented spiral bands; never hairy......................... 8
   Shell without pigmented spiral bands; sometimes hairy................. 9

8. Shell-breadth to 12 mm.; dull, chalky, white, cream or fawn; dark bands on the
   upper surface broken into a pattern of radiating blotches; dark bands on the
   lower surface numerous, fine and continuous; surface with prominent transverse
   wrinkles; umbilicus wide and deep.....................*Helicella caperata*
   Shell-breadth to 22 mm.; smooth, glossy, yellow, pinkish or reddish; up to 5
   sharp-edged dark bands severally present or absent, united or separate; parietal
   wall, umbilical area, rib and lip white; umbilicus closed......*Cepaea hortensis*

9. Umbilicus closed; shell not hairy (bandless variety)..........*Cepaea hortensis*
   Umbilicus more or less open....................................... 10

10. Umbilicus wide (diameter about 5 in least shell-breadth)................. 11
    Umbilicus narrower... 12

11. Shell hairy or pitted with microscopic scars of fallen hairs; mouth rounded-
    crescentic; H: 4·5–5 mm., B: 7–8·5 mm.; animal dark grey...*Hygromia hispida*
    Shell hairy only in young; mouth slot-crescentic; H: 6–9 mm., B: 11–13 mm.;
    animal light grey...*H. striolata*

12. Shell whitish with a contrasting brownish peristome; H: 7–12 mm., B: 12–19
    mm. 13
    Shell brownish; H: 6–7 mm., B: 9·5–12 mm........................... 14

13. Spire well elevated; whorls swollen; H: 12 mm., B: 19 mm...*Monacha cantiana*
    Spire slightly elevated; whorls not swollen; young hairy; H: 7–10 mm., B: 12–
    17 mm...*M. cartusiana*

14. Body-whorl fairly sharply keeled; spire well elevated; surface finely striated;
    H: 6–7 mm., B: 10–12 mm., W: 5–6; found in S. Devon....*Hygromia cinctella*
    Body-whorl only faintly keeled; spire slightly elevated; surface coarsely striated;
    H: 6 mm., B: 9·5 mm., W: 4½–5..........................*H. subrufescens*

15. Umbilicus wide (diameter not more than 5 in least shell-breadth).......... 16
    Umbilicus narrower 19

16. Shell hairy in young; self-coloured greyish, yellowish or reddish-horn, with a
    pale peripheral band; mouth slot-crescentic..............*Hygromia striolata*
    Shell never hairy; whitish, with numerous dark spiral bands............ 17

17. Dark bands on upper surface broken up into a pattern of radiating blotches;
    shell with prominent transverse wrinkles.................*Helicella caperata*
    Upper surface without radiating blotches; a dark band above the periphery and
    several finer bands on the lower surface............................. 18

18. Shell thick-walled, chalky; whorls not keeled; diameter of umbilicus 4 in
    least shell-breadth; found at Luddesdown (W. Kent)........*Helicella neglecta*
    Shell thin-walled; early whorls bluntly keeled; diameter of umbilicus 5 in
    least shell-breadth...*H. virgata*

19. Large species; H: greater than 10 mm., B: greater than 13 mm............ 22
    Small species; H: less than 10 mm., B: less than 13 mm................. 20

20. Shell hairy, or pitted with the microscopic scars of fallen hairs; H: less than
    7 mm., B: less than 10 mm.. 21
    Shell never hairy; reddish-brown or yellowish with a pale spiral band on the
    peripheral keel; H: 9 mm., B: 12 mm.; found in S. Devon....*Hygromia limbata*

21. Shell greenish, without other markings; surface with transverse wrinkles cock-
    ling suture; hairs short, easily rubbed off..............*Hygromia subvirescens*
    Shell greyish to yellowish white, without other markings; hairs long, very
    persistent ....*Monacha granulata*
    Shell pale horn-colour to dark reddish-brown, with a pale peripheral spiral
    band; hairs long..*H. liberta*

22. Umbilicus quite open 23
    Umbilicus considerably overhung, reduced to a cleft or quite closed....... 24

23. Shell whitish, greyish or yellowish, with or without 1 dark peripheral spiral band
    ....*Fruticicola fruticum*
    Shell whitish, with a dark peripheral spiral band and several finer dark bands on
    the lower surface...................................*Helicella virgata*

24. Shell yellow, pinkish, reddish or brownish, without markings except for a con-
    trasting rib and lip.. 25
    Shell with a pattern of dark spiral bands, or an irregular pattern formed by the
    breaking-up of such... 26

25. Lip whitish, rib white (bandless variety)...................*Cepaea hortensis*
    Lip brown-red, rib dark brown (bandless variety)...............*C. nemoralis*

26. Shell-pattern based on solid, sharp-edged dark bands................... 27
    Shell-pattern otherwise 28

27. Shell yellow, pinkish, reddish or brownish, with up to five dark bands, severally
    present or absent, united or distinct; parietal wall, umbilical region, lip and rib
    dark...*Cepaea nemoralis*
    Shell as above, but parietal wall, etc., white.....................*C. hortensis*

28. Shell breadth equals height; H and B to over 25 mm.................... 29
    Shell-breadth greater than height; B to 25 mm. 30

29. Umbilicus closed; surface coarse, with or without a gloss or glaze; colour fawn
    or light brown with up to five very broken dark brown bands crossed by zigzag
    streaks of the ground-colour; H and B to 35 mm..............*Helix aspersa*
    Umbilicus reduced to a narrow cleft; surface dull, deeply and coarsely striated;
    colour creamy with up to 5 hazy and broken dark brown bands; H and B to
    38–45 mm. or more...*H. pomatia*

30. Shell glossy, chestnut-brown to brown-yellow, with a darker peripheral band
    and many fine straw-coloured flecks...................*Arianta arbustorum*
    Shell dull, chalky, white to yellowish-white, with numerous and very variable
    dark spiral lines..*Theba pisana*

128. Bush Snail: *Fruticicola fruticum* (Müller). Shell medium-large, thin-walled, translucent, globular with an elevated conical-rounded spire; whorls convex and slightly stepped; body-whorl swollen; suture deep; mouth oblique, nearly circular, apart from curved intercept of parietal wall; peristome reflected, sharp, faced internally by a white lip; umbilicus open and deep, partly overhung by reflected columellar lip; surface slightly glossy, with fine spiral and transverse striations (lens); colour yellowish- to greyish-white or light reddish-brown, occasionally with a dark band around the periphery. H: 15–17 mm., B: 18–22 mm., W: 5–6. Animal yellow to yellowish-grey (cf. *Monacha cantiana*); lives in hedges; probably introduced into England. Distribution: Dover, Deal and Penshurst, Kent; elsewhere Europe, N. Asia.

129. Cheese Snail: *Helicodonta obvoluta* (Müller). Shell medium-sized, thick disc-shaped, rather *Planorbarius*-like, convex below, but with a flattened spire which is somewhat sunken at its centre; whorls compressed, the body-whorl rather depressed externally, sagging gently at first, but rather more steeply towards the mouth; suture deep; mouth 3-bayed; peristome sharp, inflected above, otherwise reflected and reinforced by a lip: the lip sends 2 low, broad tooth-like projections into the mouth, a stronger lateral one and a weaker lower one, and has 2 depressions on its outer surface corresponding to these; umbilicus broad in perspective; surface dull, lightly striated and covered with stiff white hairs which leave pit-like scars when they are rubbed off (lens!); colour yellowish to reddish horn-brown, with a purplish or reddish lip. H: 4–6 mm., B: 11–15 mm., W: 6½. Animal dark-grey; hides in dry weather and comes out after rain to feed on fungi, dead leaves and rotten wood. A relict species, now confined to remains of ancient beech, oak and hazel forests on calcareous soils. Distribution: S. Downs from Winchester to Rackham (W. Sussex); elsewhere Europe, N. Asia.

130. Lapidary Snail: *Helicigona lapicida* (L.). Shell medium-sized, lens-shaped, depressed, with an elevated rounded spire and a very blunt apex; body-whorl sharp-keeled, sagging suddenly and steeply towards the mouth; suture distinct; mouth elliptical, with a notch by the keel, opening downwards; peristome white, sharp, continuous, strongly reflected, and lipped all around and detached from the parietal wall; umbilicus wide; surface dull, striated and finely granulose (lens!); colour grey-brown, with dark red-brown areas, especially on the body-whorl. H: 6–7 mm., B: 17–19 mm., W: 5–6. Animal brown-grey; very secretive by day and in dry weather; lives in beech-woods, walls, hedges on calcareous soils. Distribution: local from Devon to Yorkshire (except N.W.), E. Wales, Cork; elsewhere Europe.

131. Copse Snail: *Arianta arbustorum* (L.). (Plate III.) Shell medium-large, strong-walled, globose, with an elevated conical spire and blunt apex; whorls rounded; body-whorl descends abruptly a short distance before the mouth; suture deep; mouth oblique, elongate-rounded; peristome reflected, with a thick white lip, but brownish externally; umbilicus more or

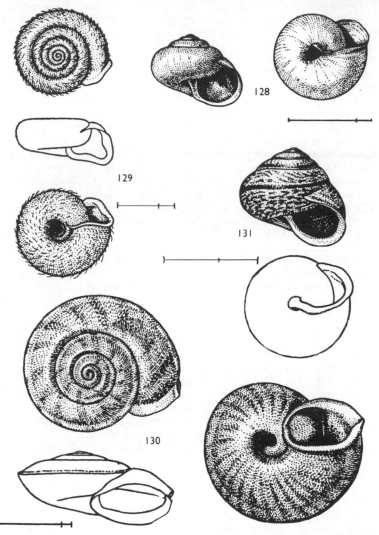

less covered by reflected columellar lip; surface glossy, irregularly striated, the striations crossed by very fine spiral lines (lens!); colour chestnut-brown to brown-yellow, with many straw-coloured flecks and a dark peripheral band. H: 12–23 mm., B: 15–25 mm., W: 5–6. Animal brown-black to dark grey; lives in moist woods (alder, willow), hedges (nettle-beds), river-banks, etc.; feeds on plants. Distribution: general in Great Britain, local in N. and C. Ireland; elsewhere N. and C. Europe.

132. Sandhill Snail; White Snail: *Theba pisana* (**Müller**). Shell medium-large, thick-walled, limy, globose-depressed, with an only slightly elevated spire and blunt apex; whorls increase rapidly, shouldered above; suture shallow; mouth broadly crescentic, nearly circular; peristome reinforced by internal rib, upper outer lip inflected, columellar lip reflected; umbilicus narrow, largely covered; surface with transverse and strong spiral striations; colour white to yellowish-white, with numerous and very variable dark spiral lines and a pink interior to the peristome. H: 15 mm., B: 18 mm., W: 5½–6. Animal translucent grey; feeds on plants and other snails, and is locally abundant on sand-dunes, cliffs and waste places near sea, remaining clinging to plants (sea holly, thistle) in dry weather or burying itself in sand (desert species abroad). Young easily confused with young *Helicigona lapicida* (*q.v.*). Distribution: Channel Islands, W. Cornwall, Dorset, Glamorgan, Pembroke, Louth, Meath, Dublin; elsewhere coasts of France, Iberia, S. Europe, N.W. Africa, Atlantic Islands.

133. Hedge Snail: *Hygromia* (*H.*) *limbata* (**Draparnaud**). Shell medium-sized, globose-depressed, with a broad rounded-conical spire; whorls evenly coiled, flattened above; body-whorl with a slight keel above the periphery; suture shallow; mouth oblique, half-moon-shaped; peristome expanded, reinforced by an internal rib behind the edge and with a strong, reflected columellar lip; umbilicus deep and very narrow, partly covered; surface glossy, with fine striations (lens); colour reddish-brown to yellowish, with a pale spiral band on the keel. H: 9 mm., B: 12 mm., W: 5½. Animal grey; feeds on mildew on dead elm leaves, etc., in damp hedges and on cliffs; sunbathes on bushes; introduced into England with cider apples. Distribution: Teign Valley and Maidencombe areas (S. Devon); elsewhere France, N. Spain.

134. Girdled Snail: *Hygromia* (*H.*) *cinctella* (**Draparnaud**). Shell small, smaller and thinner than *H. limbata*, subglobose with a well-elevated conical spire and bluntly pointed apex; whorls a little flattened, increasing regularly; body-whorl with a pronounced and fairly sharp keel at the periphery; suture shallow; mouth oblique, transversely oval, slightly transected by penultimate whorl; peristome thin, sharp, scarcely enlarged, not thickened or reflected, except that the columellar lip is reflected at its origin; umbilicus narrow; surface slightly glossy, with fine striations (lens!); colour reddish-brown or light horn-colour, with a fine opaque white peripheral band on the body-whorl. H: 6–7 mm., B: 10–12 mm., W: 5–6. Animal narrow, vermiform, slightly truncate in front, pointed behind, its length equal to one and a half times the diameter of the shell; colour yellowish-white, slightly darker in front and below, with serried lines of oval tubercles having small brown and milky points; mantle yellowish-grey, darker on neck, with very small milky points; tentacles very long (posterior 8 mm., with small knobs; anterior 2 mm. and paler), granulose, more or less yellowish-brown or greyish-white. In England lives under stones, nettles, ivy, etc., on cultivated ground or among *Mesembryanthemum* on sea-cliffs; probably introduced with exotic shrubs. Distribution: Paignton and Bishopsteignton (S. Devon); elsewhere C. and S. France. S. Alps, Mediterranean region.

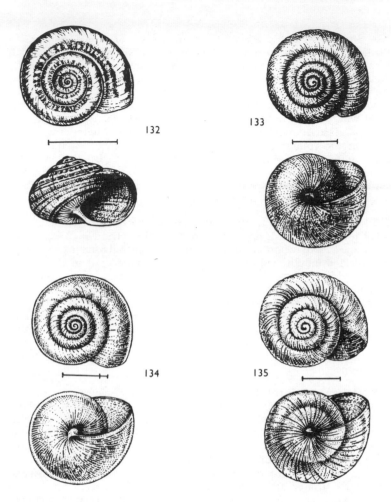

132 133

134 135

135. Brown Snail; Dusky Snail: *Hygromia* (*Zenobiella*) *subrufescens*
(**Miller**). Shell small, thin, horny, transparent, globose-depressed with a
low, blunt, conical-rounded spire; the whorls increase gradually and are
slightly stepped; body-whorl faintly keeled at periphery; suture moderate;
mouth half-moon-shaped; peristome slightly expanded, inflected above,
with a thickened and reflected columellar lip; umbilicus small, partly
covered; surface glossy, coarsely and irregularly striated (lens); amber-
coloured. H: 6 mm., B: 9·5 mm., W: 4½–5. Animal variable: yellow, black
or green-grey; local, but widespread among nettles, dog's mercury
(*Mercurialis perennis*), young alder leaves, in damp old woods and wild
places. Distribution: N. and W. of Great Britain, Ireland (except C.);
elsewhere Belgium, W. France.

136. Strawberry Snail; Ruddy Snail: *Hygromia* (*Trichia*) *striolata* (**C. Pfeiffer**). Shell medium-sized, rather strong-walled, slightly translucent, broadly depressed-globose with a low, blunt spire; body-whorl bluntly keeled above the periphery (sharper in the young), sinking a little towards the mouth; mouth roundish, rather broader than tall, blocked off by penultimate whorl; peristome thin and brittle, only slightly expanded, faced with a white translucent lip behind the edge; umbilicus wide and open; surface smooth, strongly rib-striated in the adult (lens), feebly hairy in the young; colour white-grey, yellowish-grey or reddish-horn colour, often with a pale peripheral band. H: 6–9 mm., B: 11–13 mm., W: $5\frac{3}{4}$–$6\frac{1}{4}$. Animal ash-grey; lives in damp, waste places generally, and is a garden pest (strawberry beds, etc.). Distribution: Great Britain north to Aberdeen; elsewhere W. and C. Europe.

137. Alpine Hairy Snail: *Hygromia* (*Trichia*) *liberta* (**Westerlund**). Shell small to medium-sized, depressed-globose with arched conical spire and blunt apex; body-whorl swollen, dilating and generally sinking somewhat towards the mouth; mouth rounded, slightly broader than tall, deeply transected by the penultimate whorl; peristome thin and sharp, somewhat expanded on the lower side and reinforced by a weak rib set back from the edge; umbilicus very narrow and partly covered by the reflected columellar lip; surface finely striated (lens!) and permanently covered with long (0·5 mm.) hairs; pale horn-colour to dark red-brown, sometimes with a pale peripheral band. H: 5–5·5 mm., B: 7–7·5 mm., W: 5–$5\frac{1}{3}$. Lives in woods, hedges, etc. Distribution: C. England; elsewhere Alpine regions of C. Europe.

138. Hairy Snail; Bristly Snail: *Hygromia* (*Trichia*) *hispida* (**L.**). Shell small to medium-sized, not very thin-walled, translucent, very depressed-globose, with a blunt, slightly elevated spire; body-whorl slightly blunt-keeled, sinking a little towards the mouth; mouth oval moon-shaped; peristome sharp, slightly reflected, expanded underneath, where there is a strong white internal rib continued superficially round the sides; umbilicus wide to very wide; surface dull to slightly glossy (according to hairiness), irregularly striated and feebly covered with short, recurved white periostracal hairs which leave scars where they rub off (lens!); colour grey-brown to reddish-brown with a pale peripheral zone. H: 4·5–5 mm., B: 7–8·5 mm., W: 6–7. Animal dark grey; common under moss, stones, logs, etc., in wild and cultivated places. Distribution: Great Britain north to Kincardine, Hebrides, Orkney, Ireland; elsewhere Europe.

139. Green Hairy Snail: *Hygromia* (*Pomentina*) *subvirescens* (**Bellamy**). Shell small, very thin-walled, semitransparent, globose, little depressed, with a slightly elevated spire; whorls convex; body-whorl large, but not dilated towards the mouth; suture deep, apparently cockled by transverse striations; mouth nearly circular; peristome scarcely thickened, upper outer lip somewhat inflected, columellar lip reflected; umbilicus narrow, partly covered; surface transversely striated (lens) and covered with very fine,

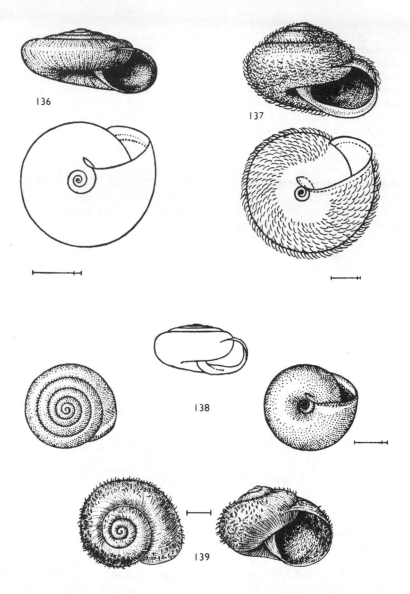

136

137

138

139

short white periostracal hairs, which easily rub off; colour greenish (camouflage). H: 4·5 mm., B: 6 mm., W: 4–4½. Animal dark yellowish-grey; feeds on plants and lives on grassy slopes near sea. Distribution: S.W. England, Pembroke; elsewhere Channel Isles, W. France, Spain, Portugal, N.W. Africa.

140. Chartreuse Snail; Carthusian Snail: *Monacha* (*M.*) *cartusiana* (**Müller**). Shell medium-sized, thin-walled, slightly translucent, globose, depressed above, more convex below, with a slightly elevated conical spire; the body-whorl has the bare suggestion of a keel above the periphery and sinks a little towards the mouth, where it is twice as broad as the previous whorl; suture deep; mouth rounded-crescentic; peristome sharp, scarcely expanded, internally reinforced near the edge by a strong rib and with a slightly reflected columellar lip; umbilicus very narrow, half-covered; surface smooth, glossy, with faint transverse striations (lens); colour milky greyish-white to yellowish-white, sometimes with a paler peripheral band, the rib internally pale reddish-brown and externally pale yellowish-white or reddish-yellow, contrasting with the brownish mouth-region. H: 7–10 mm., B: 12–17 mm., W: 5½–6¼. Animal yellowish-grey; lives on grassy banks and downs on calcareous soils. Distribution: Hampshire, Sussex, Kent, Suffolk; elsewhere W. and S. Europe.

141. Kentish Snail: *Monacha* (*M.*) *cantiana* (**Montagu**). Shell medium-large, as compared with *M. cartusiana* larger, thinner-walled, more transparent, more globose, with fuller whorls and a more elevated spire; the body-whorl is well rounded and expands a little just before the mouth, where it is slightly more than twice as broad as the previous whorl; suture deep; mouth rounded-crescentic; peristome sharp, scarcely expanded, internally reinforced by a white rib set back from the edge; umbilicus narrow, deep; surface glossy with fine transverse striations (hairy covering of young soon lost) (lens!); colour whitish or yellowish-white, tinged with reddish on the lower surface and towards the mouth, with a brownish peristome and sometimes a pale peripheral band. H: 12 mm., B: 19 mm., W: 6–6½. Animal pale brown; feeds on decaying vegetation among nettles, grass and brambles on calcareous soils. Distribution: Devon to Durham, Glamorgan; elsewhere W. Europe.

142. Silky Snail: *Monacha* (*Ashfordia*) *granulata* (**Alder**). Shell small, thin, horny, translucent, conical-globose with a well-elevated spire; whorls well rounded, increasing gradually; body-whorl falling slightly towards the mouth, where it is not dilated and is about one and a half times the breadth of the previous whorl; suture deep; mouth obliquely semicircular; peristome thin, sharp, with a weak white rib set back from the edge; umbilicus very narrow, partly covered; surface slightly glossy, covered with very persistent long, stiff, whitish hairs whose bulbous bases are arranged in oblique rows, crossing the lines of growth (lens!); colour greyish to yellowish-white, without any pale peripheral band. H: 5·5 mm., B: 7·5 mm., W: 5½–6. Animal has a translucent, whitish, granular body sprinkled with opaque white specks; lives among herbage in damp places. Distribution: England and Wales, sparse in Scotland, rare in S.W. Ireland; apparently endemic (i.e. not found abroad).

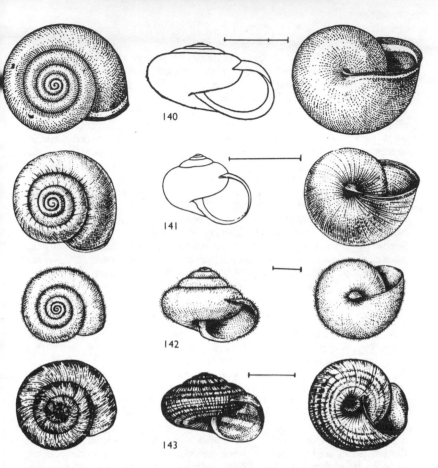

140

141

142

143

143. Wrinkled Snail: *Helicella* (*Candidula*) *caperata* (**Montagu**). Shell medium-sized, solid, limy, depressed-globose, with an elevated blunt conical spire; whorls increasing slowly and regularly; body-whorl well rounded, not dilated towards the mouth, where it is about twice the breadth of the previous whorl; suture fairly deep; mouth semicircular, oblique; peristome thin, not expanded, with a strong white internal rib; insertion of columellar lip rather steep and its junction with the outer lip rather angular; umbilicus wide, deep and central; surface dull, with many strong, irregular transverse striations (lens); colour white or cream to pale fawn above, with several broken spiral purple-brown bands, forming a pattern of radiating heavy blotches on the upper surface, but more numerous, finer and much less broken on the lower; there is sometimes a continuous band at the periphery. H: 8 mm., B: 12 mm., W: 4½–5. Species generally distributed on downs, grassy banks, etc., on calcareous soils; feeds on dead plants (yarrow) and appear in crowds after rain. Distribution: British Isles; elsewhere W. Europe.

127

144. Eccentric Snail: *Helicella* (*Candidula*) *gigaxi* (L. Pfeiffer). Shell medium-sized, depressed-globose, with a scarcely elevated rounded spire; whorls increasing regularly, but more rapidly than in *H. caperata*; body-whorl distinctly dilated towards the mouth, where it is a little more than twice the breadth of the previous whorl; suture shallow; mouth broadly elliptical-crescentic, oblique; peristome thin, sharp, not expanded, with a weak pink internal rib; insertion of columellar lip rather oblique and its junction with the outer lip forming a smooth, continuous curve; umbilicus wide in perspective, deep and rather eccentric; surface dull, with many fine, close, regular transverse striations (lens); colour cream to creamy-brown, with several broken, dark spiral bands, on the upper surface faint towards the insides of the whorls, but clearer and more continuous towards the outsides, on the lower surface continuous but less numerous and less heavily pigmented than in *H. caperata*. H: 7 mm., B: 14 mm., W: 4½–5. Species lives in dry grassy places on calcareous soils and feeds on dead plants; more given to climbing and tolerant of drought than *H. caperata*. Distribution: England (except S.W. and N.W.), N. Wales, Glamorgan, Berwick, Haddington; elsewhere W. Europe.

145. Banded Snail: *Helicella* (*Cernuella*) *virgata* (da Costa). Shell medium-large, thin-walled, slightly translucent, slightly depressed-globose, with a well-elevated conical spire; whorls increasing regularly, the early ones bluntly keeled; body-whorl loses keel and increases rapidly towards mouth; mouth oblique, rounded; peristome sharp, three-quarters circular, slightly reflected with a brown or white rib inside the edge; umbilicus, diameter about 5 in least breadth of shell, deep, slightly covered; surface smooth, slightly glossy, especially at the apex, with fine, irregular striations; colour white to cream with a brown apex, a heavy dark brown band above the periphery and several very fine, broken bands on the underside. H: 13 mm., B: 16 mm., W: 5–6. Lives on dry downs, banks, sand dunes, etc., on calcareous soils, and is said to be deliberately eaten by sheep. Distribution: England and Wales, Scotland north to Aberdeen (sparse), Ireland (except N.W.); elsewhere W. Europe and Mediterranean countries.

146. Luddesdown Snail: *Helicella* (*Xerocincta*) *neglecta* (Draparnaud). Shell medium-sized, thick-walled, chalky, depressed-globose, with an elevated conical spire; body-whorl increasing considerably towards the mouth; mouth oblique, circular-elliptical; peristome expanded, sharp, with a thick, brown rib inside the edge; diameter of umbilicus about 4 in least breadth of shell; surface with fine, regular striations; colour white with a broad dark band above the periphery and several finer and less distinct bands on the lower surface. H: 10 mm., B: 14 mm., W: 5. Lives on chalk banks, very local and probably introduced. Distribution: Luddesdown (W. Kent); elsewhere France, Catalonia and Mediterranean countries.

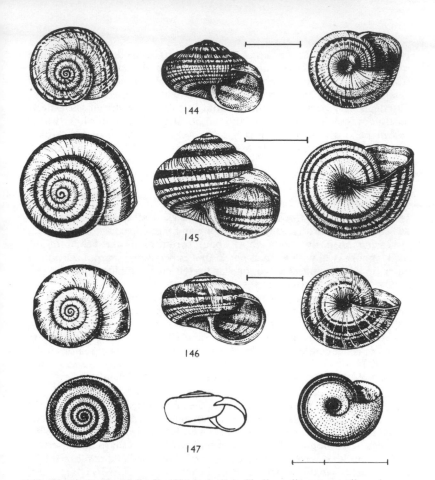

147. Heath Snail: *Helicella* (*H.*) *itala* (**L.**). Shell medium to medium-large, fairly thick-walled, limy, slightly translucent between the bands, thick, disc-shaped, with a very slightly elevated conical spire; whorls increasing regularly; body-whorl sinking below the periphery of the previous one and increasing slightly towards the mouth; mouth oblique, circular-elliptical; peristome sharp, distinctly expanded, especially beneath, forming four-fifths of a circle, and with a very weak internal rib; umbilicus broad in perspective, diameter about 3 in least breadth of shell; surface slightly glossy, with fine striations; colour white to cream, with pale to dark horn-brown bands comprising a broader one above the periphery and several narrower ones on the lower surface; occasionally self-coloured. H: 5–12 mm., B: 9–25 mm., W: 5¼–6. Lives on dry downs, pastures and sand-dunes on calcareous soils; remains attached to grasses, thistles, etc., in dry weather. Distribution: England, Ireland, north and south coasts of Wales, S.E., W. and N. Scotland; elsewhere Europe.

129

148. Top Snail: *Helicella* (*Trochoidea*) *elegans* (**Gmelin**). Shell small, quite conical, with a flattened underside, much like the marine Top Shells (*Calliostoma*); whorls increasing regularly, sharply keeled; mouth oblique, elongate-elliptical; peristome sharp, with a slightly reflected columellar lip; umbilicus very narrow, diameter about 9 in least breadth of shell, deep, partly covered; surface evenly and closely striated; colour white, with a brown band above the periphery and several fine, more or less broken bands on the underside. H: 6 mm., B: 7·5 mm., W: 5–6. Introduced; lives on chalk banks and hillsides. Distribution: near Dover (Kent) and Chaldon (Surrey); elsewhere S. France to Bordeaux, Mediterranean countries.

149. Pointed Snail: *Cochlicella acuta* (**Müller**). Shell medium-large, thin-walled, elongate, with a long conical spire and blunt apex; whorls rounded, increasing regularly; body-whorl about two-fifths of the height of the shell; mouth oval with a small notch above; peristome sharp, insertion of outer lip slightly inflected, columellar lip reflected; umbilicus narrow and almost completely covered; surface dull, with faint, irregular striations; colour dirty white, with brown transverse streaks and a dark spiral band below the periphery, which may be variously confined to the body-whorl, duplicated or absent. H: 15–26 mm., B: 5·5–7 mm., W: 9. Lives on dry, calcareous grassy banks, downs and sandhills; clings to grasses in dry weather; is deliberately eaten by sheep. Distribution: coastal regions in S., W. and N. of Great Britain, coastal regions and centre of Ireland; elsewhere S.W. Europe, Mediterranean Region, Atlantic Islands.

150. Grove Snail; Brown-lipped Snail: *Cepaea nemoralis* (**L.**). (Plate III.) Shell large, fairly thick-walled, globose, slightly depressed, with an elevated, rounded spire and a blunt apex; whorls rounded, increasing rapidly and regularly; mouth irregularly crescentic; peristome sharp, the insertion of the outer lip somewhat inflected, otherwise reflected and reinforced by a dark internal rib; umbilicus narrow in the young, closed in the adult; surface glossy, often becoming duller with age, with fine, irregular striations; ground colour typically clear yellow, otherwise one of many shades of white, pink, reddish or brown, with typically 5 sharp-edged brown to black spiral bands, of which the 3 narrower ones are above the periphery and the 2 broader ones below; umbilical region, parietal wall and inside and outside of peristome black-brown; lip brown-red. H: 15–20 mm., B: 17–26 mm., W: 5½. Animal lead-grey, tinged yellow, with a pale yellow mantle. There is much variation in the banding; any one of the 5 bands may be absent, present and separate, or present and joined to the adjacent one, giving 89 possible combinations. A notation has been devised to describe any observed condition. A shell with all 5 bands present and separate is represented thus: 12345. A shell with the second band missing and the fourth and fifth joined is represented thus; 103(45). In addition, a faint band may be indicated by a : in the corresponding position and a split band by a repetition of the appropriate number in smaller type. Much

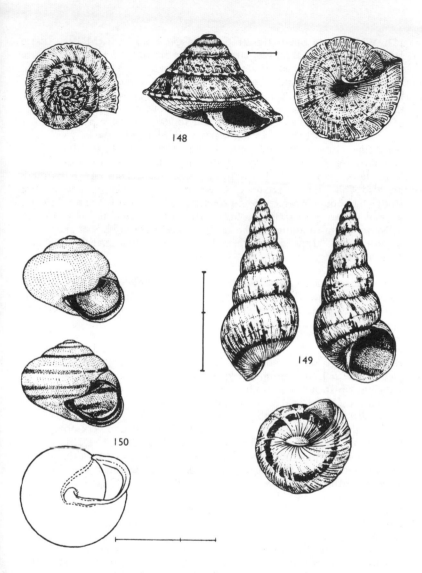

148

149

150

research has been devoted to the inheritance of band-forms, the incidence of various combinations in various local populations and the relative protective value of the various patterns (these snails are frequent victims on blackbirds' and thrushes' altar-stones). Lives in woods, copses, hedges, etc. Distribution: British Isles, except N. and N.E. Scotland; elsewhere Europe.

151. White-lipped Snail; Garden Snail: *Cepaea hortensis* (Müller). (Plate III.) Shell medium-large, very similar to *C. nemoralis*, from which it differs in being thinner-walled, slightly smaller, squatter and in having more rounded whorls; mouth crescentic; peristome thickened, reflected and reinforced with a white internal rib; umbilicus covered; surface glossier than *C. nemoralis*; ground-colour typically yellow, but with the same range of colour-variations as *C. nemoralis* and similarly variable patterns based on 5 dark spiral bands (see above); umbilical region, parietal wall and peristome whitish, rib pure white. H: 15–16 mm., B: 16–22 mm., W: 5. Animal greenish-grey, yellowish posteriorly, with a grey or yellow mantle. Black-lipped individuals do occur, and since (in Ireland especially) there are also white-lipped variants of *C. nemoralis*, identification may require study of a population-sample or dissection and examination of the dart and vaginal mucus glands (Figure 5). Distribution: general in Great Britain (fills the vacant sand-dune niche left by *C. nemoralis* in N. Scotland), local in N.E. and C. Ireland; elsewhere Europe, extending farther north than *C. nemoralis*.

152. Roman Snail; Apple Snail; Vine Snail; Edible Snail: *Helix* (*H.*) *pomatia* L. (Plate IV.) Our largest British snail. Shell very large, thick-walled, with a more or less elevated, blunt, conical spire and a rounded apex; whorls rounded; body-whorl large, swollen, accounting for over four-fifths of the shell-height; mouth rounded, taller than broad, pointed above; peristome blunt, thickened, slightly expanded and reflected and reinforced by a weak white to reddish lip; umbilicus reduced to a narrow cleft by the reflected columellar lip; surface coarser than *H. aspersa*, with irregular rib-striations; colour cream, greyish-white or pale yellow-brown, with up to 5 fuzzy, pale brown, spiral bands (usually :(23)45; see *Cepaea nemoralis*). H and B: 38–45 mm. (more or less), W: 5. Animal very large and rough, pale yellow-grey with a yellowish mantle and very broad foot. In addition to the normal dextral shell (illustrations 152, 152b), we also illustrate a sinistral specimen (No. 152a). During hibernation this species closes the mouth of its shell with a chalky false operculum or epiphragm (*pomatia*, from Greek *poma*, a door), which it casts off again next spring (No. 152c, Plate IV). For courtship and egg-laying, see pages 18, 164. Since the time of the Romans, this species has been kept and fattened as a delicacy. There is a substantial mythology concerning its introduction into this country; be that as it may, subfossil remains show that it was certainly here long before the Romans arrived. Lives in open woods, quarries, on downs, banks, etc., on calcareous soils, but not on cultivated land. Distribution: south of the line Severn–Wash, but not S.W. England; elsewhere Europe.

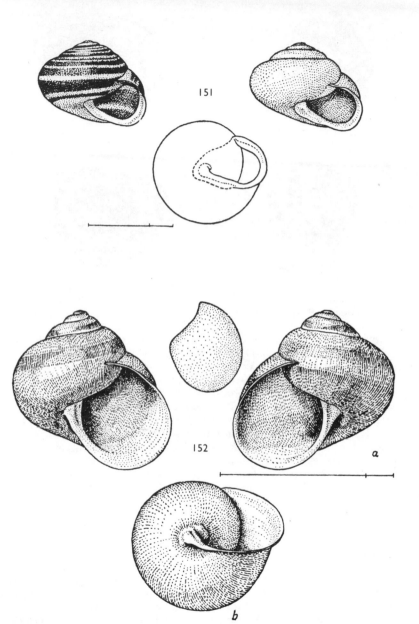

151

152

a

b

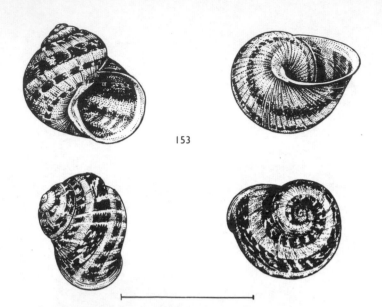

153

153. Common Snail: *Helix* (*Cornu*) *aspersa* **Müller.** Shell large, more or less thick-walled, much like *H. pomatia*, except that the whorls are less swollen and a trifle depressed; peristome white, expanded and reflected, with a thickened lip; umbilicus quite closed in the adult; surface rough, with finer striations than in *H. pomatia*, glossy or with a matt glaze in young specimens and favoured adults, but usually very shabby; ground-colour fawn, buff or yellowish with up to 5 spiral dark-brown bands, which are variously combined or omitted and interrupted by zigzag streaks of the ground-colour or thoroughly broken up to give a mottled appearance. The bands appear much more distinct and sharp-edged from the inside of the shell. H: 35 mm., B: 35 mm., W: 4½–5. Sinistral specimens and cornucopia-shaped freaks also occur. The animal is rough, slenderer than *H. pomatia*, dark grey, with a darker mantle finely spotted with yellowish-grey. Breeding-biology much like *H. pomatia*, except that the courtship is less protracted and the eggs smaller and more numerous. *H. aspersa* has a pronounced homing-instinct, and is more gregarious than *H. pomatia*, "roosting" in large groups under stones, etc., and similarly hibernating. The epiphragm (see above) is composed of several layers of hardened mucus. The species has a remarkable capacity for repairing damage to its shell. It is abundant in gardens, but does relatively little damage except to fruit. Edible; snail-hunting festivals used to be held in rural districts, and even today the species sometimes deputises for *H. pomatia* in epicurean restaurants. Distribution: British Isles, more or less general, except in N. Scotland; elsewhere W. Europe, Mediterranean and Black Sea regions, Atlantic Islands.

134

Part Five
How to Identify Mussels

As might be expected from the fundamental differences in structure and form, the diagnostic characters to be determined and compared in identifying mussels are quite different from those employed in snails (Figures 9, 24). First of all, we have to distinguish the anterior from the posterior ends and the right from the left sides. This may appear difficult at first sight unless we have the opportunity to observe the direction of motion in the living animal, but even in a dead shell there are good reference-points. In all our native fresh-water mussels we can rely on the fact that the hinge-ligament lies posterior to the umbones, and by arranging the shells accordingly we can then distinguish left from right.

The dorsal and ventral sides are easily distinguished, since the umbones are dorsal. These are the oldest parts of the shell and, being also the thinnest, are sometimes considerably eroded as in *Margaritifera*. The umbones may be more or less prominent, depending upon whether they are strongly elevated or inflated or broadly and slightly arched. They may also be more or less strongly elevated above the general profile of the shell. Sometimes the embryonal shell may persist as a tiny cap on the outside of the umbo, as in *Sphaerium lacustre*, and frequently the umbones of young animals are variously sculptured with more or less concentric simple or forked ridges, though these usually disappear with age.

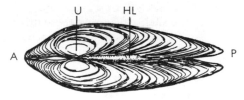

Figure 24. Freshwater mussel shell viewed from above. A anterior and P posterior ends, HL hinge-ligament, U umbo.

We have also to notice the colour and texture of the insides and outsides of the valves, and whether the outer surfaces are smooth, coarsely or finely striated or ribbed, whether there are further concentric markings indicating the annual interruptions in growth, and whether there is anything strikingly characteristic in the general form.

The structure of the hinge is also very important in determining species (Figure 9). The hinge consists of the inner side of the upper edge of each shell-valve, the *hinge-plate*, and the tooth- or ridge-like

135

prominences situated thereon which engage with pits, furrows, etc., on the opposite valve. Regardless of form, all such elevations are termed *teeth*, and those lying immediately ventral to the umbones are further designated *cardinal teeth* (*c*) while those further removed from the umbones are termed *anterior* (*a*) and *posterior* (*p*) *lateral teeth* respectively. (It is also quite possible to have a hinge-ridge without teeth, as in *Anodonta*.) Various notations have been devised to facilitate brief and easy shorthand reference to the various hinge-teeth, and the one we shall use here is best explained by the following diagram:

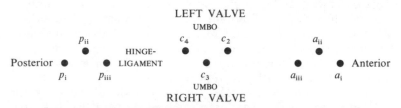

Note that the cardinal teeth are numbered from the front backwards and in Arabic figures; the anterior and posterior lateral teeth are numbered towards the umbo and in Roman figures; all the even-numbered teeth are on the left valve and all the odd-numbered ones on the right valve. If a cardinal tooth happens to be forked, the anterior and posterior divisions are indicated by the Greek letters α (alpha) and β (beta) respectively. Sometimes, also, we may have to take note of a shelly mass or *callus* such as lies between p_{iii} and the ligament-pit in *Pisidium personatum*.

We have already observed some of the muscle-scars on the insides of the shell-valves and these now require more detailed attention. Again we can identify them by a theoretical diagram, to be carefully compared with Figure 9.

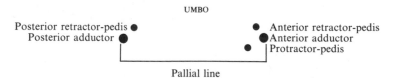

We have already noticed the two adductor muscles (Figure 8, page 18) and know that they are concerned with closing the valves of the shell, working in opposition to the tension of the hinge-ligament about the hinge-teeth as fulcra or pivots. Now we meet the two retractor-pedis muscles which are responsible for withdrawing the foot into the shell, and the protractor-pedis which protrudes the foot from the shell. All these muscles leave scars on the insides of the shell-valves which vary greatly in shape, size, depth, surface-texture and degree of separation or coalescence, and accordingly afford further clues to the identification of species.

We must also mention the pallial line. This is the line on the inside of each valve which marks the position of the mantle-edge in the contracted condition and where, naturally, there is a greater deposition of shell-substance than anywhere else.

In giving the measurements of the shell we must employ a different notation from the one we used for snails. The letters and figures accordingly indicate the following measurements in millimetres:

L = length of shell.

H = height or depth of shell.

B = breadth of shell across both valves.

The anatomy of the soft parts is not much used in the identification of species, but can provide some useful clues to families and genera. Thus we can notice that the foot is tongue- or wedge-shaped in the Margaritiferidae and Unionidae, but long and slender in the Sphaeriidae. Again, in the two former families the inhalant and exhalant openings (Figure 8) do not form tubes, but in the Sphaeriidae the mantle is produced into long, tubular siphons, 2 in *Sphaerium* and 1 (shorter) in *Pisidium*. In the Dreissenidae the animal secretes a byssus, or tuft of threads, by which it attaches itself to stones, piles, etc., like the marine mussels (*Mytilus*), but all our other freshwater mussels are free-living, at least as adults, and do not have a byssus. All these points, together with the colours of the foot and siphons, should be noted from living specimens.

A few freshwater mussels are quite stable in form, but most are extraordinarily variable in association with the hardness and rate of flow of the water, etc., a phenomenon which requires a great deal more investigation. We have done our best with them in the space available here, but must frankly admit that that means very little. Serious students should therefore consult A. E. Ellis's *Synopsis* (page 3), which is an authoritative work, devoting as much space and as many illustrations to mussels alone as we have at our disposal in this entire book, and one which has furnished most of the information needed to supplement Dr. Janus's original text. Ellis remarks of the Unionacea: "The determination of the species . . . does not lend itself to treatment in a dichotomous key." We heartily agree, though we tempt Providence with the following:

1. Shell large to very large (length to much more than 50 mm.)............. 2
   Shell small to very small (length exceptionally to 50 mm.).............. 7

2. Hinge without teeth; shell with postero-dorsal wings (*Anodonta*)........... 3
   Hinge with teeth; shell without postero-dorsal wings................... 5

3. Scar of posterior retractor-pedis incorporated in scar of posterior adductor,
   forming a common, broad, inverted, comma-shaped scar; dorsal and ventral
   margins diverging strongly from before backwards; hindmost point well below
   centre of valve; shell markedly swollen, dark greenish-grey to green-brown,
   growing to 100 mm. in length; animal prefers sandy bottoms in flowing water
   .... *Anodonta anatina*
   Shell disagreeing with most of the above characters..................... 4

4. Scar of posterior retractor-pedis more or less detached from scar of posterior
   adductor, and at most united with it by a narrow "neck"; both scars irregularly
   quadrangular; dorsal margin very level and almost parallel to ventral in adult
   (more divergent in young); hindmost point on a level with centre of valve; shell
   not swollen, except in very old individuals, yellow or yellowish-green, growing
   to 140 mm. in length; animal prefers muddy bottoms in still water...........
   ....*Anodonta cygnaea*
   Scar of posterior retractor-pedis coalescent with that of the posterior adductor,
   both scars rounded and together forming a sugarloaf-shape without a distinct
   neck; dorsal margin diverging somewhat from the ventral posteriorly, but much
   less markedly than in *A. anatina*; ventral margin more deeply and smoothly
   curved than in *A. cygnaea*; hindmost point about on a level with centre of valve;
   shell not swollen, dark olive-green to moss-green, growing to 90 mm. in length;
   animal local in rivers and some canals from Surrey through the Midlands to
   Yorkshire..*Anodonta complanata*

5. Umbones depressed (usually much eroded as well), merging smoothly into the
   profile and surface of the shell; scars of posterior retractor-pedis and posterior
   adductor forming a common broadly elliptical scar; postero-dorsal and ventral
   margins usually concave......................*Margaritifera margaritifera*
   Umbones swollen and elevated; scars of posterior retractor-pedis and posterior
   adductor coalescing to form an irregular sugar-loaf shape; postero-dorsal and
   ventral margins various, but not concave (*Unio*)........................ 6

6. Shell rectangular-elongate (depth less than half of length); a wide postero-dorsal
   gape between the valves; hinge-ligament narrow.............. *Unio pictorum*
   Shell oval (depth about half the length), markedly swollen; a narrow postero-
   dorsal gape between the valves; hinge-ligament wide........... *Unio tumidus*

7. Shell elongate, almost triangular; length 20–50 mm.; attached to stones, etc.,
   by a byssus (tuft of threads)........................ *Dreissena polymorpha*
   Shell rounded or oval; length exceptionally over 20 mm., but usually much less;
   adult animal free-living, not attached by a byssus...................... 8

8. Umbones anterior to centre; length over 10 mm.; 2 long siphons (*Sphaerium*) 9
   Umbones posterior to centre; length usually less than 10 mm.; 1 short siphon
   (*Pisidium*)... 12

9. Shell thin, fragile; umbones capped by embryonic shell..... *Sphaerium lacustre*
   Shell thicker; umbones not capped by embryonic shell.................. 10

10. Shell thick, solid; length 16–27 mm.................... *Sphaerium rivicola*
    Shell thin, smooth; length usually less than 16 mm.................... 11

11. Shell rounded or subglobose, swollen................... *Sphaerium corneum*
    Shell oblong, compressed............................... *S. transversum*

12. Adult shell-length 8–13 mm.; shell strongly striated; anterior part much longer
    than posterior; lateral teeth in right valve parallel; fairly generally distributed
    and common... *Pisidium amnicum*
    Adult shell-length 1·5–7 mm.. 13

13. Umbo with a ridge or crest.. 14
    Umbo without a ridge or crest..................................... 16

14. Adult shell-length only 1·5 mm.; shape rather quadrangular; a collar-like ridge
    below each umbo; hinge strong; p_{iii} incurved towards the umbo; ligament-pit
    vaguely-defined; absent from Scotland and rare in Ireland... *P. moitessierianum*
    Adult shell-length 3–6 mm.; umbo with a posterior ridge; umbones well elevated
    and narrow; ligament-pit long and narrow........................... 15

15. Shell-length greater than depth; shell thin, with close, regular striations; hinge
    weak.. *P. henslowanum*
    Shell-length equal to or slightly less than depth; shell thick, triangular in shape,
    with fairly strong, well-spaced striations; hinge-plate broad, with strong teeth;
    England, except S. and S.W................................. *P. supinum*

16. Shell oblong or rhomboidal with a nearly straight lower edge, swollen, glossy,
    with strong irregular striations; hinge-plate narrow; cardinal hinge-teeth long
    and straight; ligament-pit long, narrow and rather indistinct; generally distri-
    buted.. *P. millum*
    Shell oval or triangular.. 17

17. Callus present between posterior lateral teeth and ligament-pit; shell oval,
    equilateral (umbones practically central), rather compressed, with faint stria-
    tions; surface silky, not glossy; generally distributed.......... *P. personatum*
    Hinge-plate without a callus....................................... 18

18. p_{iii} very short, curving inwards towards the umbo above p_i and ending in a knob
    or pseudo-callus; shell swollen, inequilateral (umbones well behind centre) and
    glossy; hinge very short; a_{iii} very small...................... *P. obtusale*
    p_{iii} without pseudo-callus..................................... 19

19. Shell with deep and regular striations and iridescent; hinge strong; lateral teeth
    stout; cardinal teeth long and curved; c_3 thickened posteriorly and often clavate
    (club-shaped); general but local........................... *P. pulchellum*
    Striations relatively weak... 20

139

20. Shell inequilateral (umbones well behind centre), posterior end short 21
    Shell equilateral, or with umbones only slightly posterior 23

21. Shell-length not more than 2 mm.; shell thick with very regular striations; hinge
    stout; lateral teeth robust; a_{ii} and p_{ii} nearly same distance from c_2; rivers and
    canals in Midlands and E. Wales, rare .... *P. tenuilineatum*
    Shell-length more than 2 mm.; striations less regular; hinge weaker, less
    arched 22

22. Shell glossy, with even striations; posterior end very short; umbones oblique;
    c_2 and c_4 long, straight and parallel; c_4 overlaps c_2 at both ends; anterior lateral
    teeth close to cardinals; ligament-pit wider posteriorly; generally distributed ...
    .... *P. subtruncatum*
    Shell silky, not glossy; umbones narrow; ligament-pit narrow; c_2 and c_3 curved;
    c_2 and c_4 not parallel .... *P. henslowanum* var. *nucleus*

23. Ligament-pit long and narrow 24
    Ligament-pit broad 26

24. Shell almost pentagonal, swollen, glossy, with strong striations and over 3 mm.
    in length; umbones prominent; hinge strong; p_i and p_{iii} converging in front;
    lakes in N. Wales, N. England, Scotland and Ireland .... *P. lilljeborgii*
    Shell rounded, rather compressed, with faint striations; umbones depressed;
    hinge narrow; shell-length about 3 mm. 25

25. Shell very thin and fragile; cardinal teeth overhang hinge-plate; a_{iii} and p_{iii} very
    small; in cold lakes in Caernarvon, Lake District, Perth, Inverness, Kerry .....
    .... *P. conventum*
    Shell thin; umbones well behind centre (shell resembles a miniature *Sphaerium*
    corneum back-to-front); hinge like *P. milium*; local in marsh drains and lakes in
    Sussex, Somerset and Cheshire .... *P. pseudosphaerium*

26. Shell very glossy, with moderate to strong striations; umbo smooth, bounded
    by 3 deep grooves; cardinal teeth short; lateral teeth long and parallel; ligament-
    pit short and moderately wide; generally distributed .... *P. nitidum*
    Shell not glossy, lacking umbonal grooves; cardinal teeth long 27

27. Shell striations close and regular; umbones (juvenile shell) with concentric
    striations and radiating flecks; shell very swollen, equilateral (umbones nearly
    central); umbones prominent and surrounded by 3–5 faint grooves; cardinal
    teeth long and nearly straight; ligament-pit short and broad; generally distri-
    buted, but rarer in the south .... *P. hibernicum*
    Shell striations fine, vague and irregular; shell slightly inequilateral (umbones
    slightly behind centre); shell-length to 7 mm.; umbones broad and slightly pro-
    jecting; hinge strong; c_2 and c_3 curved; ligament-pit long and broad; the com-
    monest and most general British species .... *P. casertanum*

Apart from minor simplifications, amendments and additions, the above key to
Pisidium is taken from Ellis (1962).

Class Lamellibranchiata
(Bivalve Molluscs)

SUPERFAMILY UNIONACEA

Family Margaritiferidae (Pearl Mussels)

Large freshwater mussels, having an elongate shell with rather low umbones and very few well-developed hinge-teeth. In their internal anatomy these animals display a number of primitive features; for example, the inhalant and exhalant openings are incompletely separated and do not form siphons, and the junctions between the gill-lamellae (page 22) are indiscriminately scattered, so that no clearly defined water-tubes are formed. The foot is stout and wedge-like. We have a single British species.

154. Pearl Mussel: *Margaritifera margaritifera* (**L.**). Shell outline elongate, somewhat kidney-shaped through a slight concavity of the lower margin; postero-dorsal margin slightly arched at first, but sloping steeply and concave towards the blunt-pointed hinder end; umbones low, usually much corroded away and seemingly worm-eaten; hinge-teeth a_{iii} in right valve, a_{ii} and c_4 in left; inside with an iridescent mother-of-pearl layer. Colour yellow-brown through dark brown to black, according to age. L: 120–150 mm., H: 55–72 mm., B: 32–45 mm. Occasionally forms pearls; British pearl-fisheries famous in Roman times. *Glochidium* larvae parasitic on gills of trout, minnow and miller's thumb (*Cottus gobio*). A soft-water species, preferring sandy bottoms of lime-poor streams running off ancient igneous and sandstone rocks. Distribution: British Isles, except C. Ireland, E. Scottish Lowlands and the region south of the line Scarborough–Beer Head; elsewhere Holarctic, except Mediterranean region.

120-150mm

154

Family Unionidae (*River Mussels*)

Large freshwater mussels having an elongate to broadly oval shell with rather prominent to swollen umbones and a hinge with several more or less well-developed teeth or none. The shell-form is very variable in most species in relation to environmental conditions. The inhalant and exhalant openings are completely separated, though they do not form siphons. The gill-lamellae (page 22) are joined by regular vertical septa so as to form clearly defined water-tubes, which are used as egg-sacs in the marsupial gills of the female. The foot is stout and wedge-like. The descriptions below supplement the information already given in the key (*q.v.*). We have 5 British species belonging to 2 genera.

155. Painter's Mussel: *Unio pictorum* (L.). Shell rather swollen anteriorly, compressed posteriorly; outline rounded anteriorly, elongate, tapering and bluntly pointed posteriorly; length more than twice the height; umbones inflated; hinge-teeth in right valve rudimentary a_i, a_{iii} (rudimentary c_3), p_{iii}, in left valve a_{ii}, c_2, p_{ii}, p_{iv}. Colour yellowish-green to brown, with diverging ray-like markings in young. L: 60–140 mm., H: 25–60 mm., B: 23–31 mm. Shells formerly used by artists to hold their pigments. A hard-water species, living in rivers, canals, lakes and large ponds. Distribution: Exeter Canal to Northumberland, Brecon, Montgomery; elsewhere Palaearctic, except parts of Mediterranean region.

156. Swollen River Mussel: *Unio tumidus* Philipsson. Shell very swollen anteriorly, pointed wedge-shaped posteriorly; outline elongate-oval; length twice the height or a little less; umbones inflated and elevated; hinge-teeth much as in *U. pictorum* and similarly long-based, but taller with striking crests instead of flat tops. Colour greenish to dark brown, sometimes with alternating light and dark zones and yellowish rays. L: 65–80 mm. (exceptionally to 130 mm.), H: 30–40 mm., B: 24–28 mm. A hard-water species, living in slow rivers and canals. Distribution: Somerset and Kent to Yorkshire (except East Anglia), Brecon, Montgomery; elsewhere W. and C. Europe, W. Asia.

157. Swan Mussel: *Anodonta cygnaea* (L.). Shell not swollen, except occasionally in old individuals; outline elongate-oval with wing-like or blade-like postero-dorsal processes contributing to a very level dorsal margin, which is almost parallel to the straight mid-ventral edge; hindmost point on a level with centre of shell; umbones only slightly swollen; ridges, but no hinge-teeth. Young shell more like *A. anatina* (*q.v.*). The form is very variable in this genus, and the muscle-scar characters in the key are among the most reliable. Colour typically yellow to yellowish-green, but again variable. L: 95–200 mm., H: 60–120 mm., B: 30–60 mm., exceptionally larger. Prefers hard water and muddy bottoms in slow rivers, canals, lakes and large ponds. Distribution: from Exeter Canal over most of England and locally north to Moray, S. Wales, Montgomery, Anglesey, Ireland, except S. and S.W.; elsewhere Palaearctic.

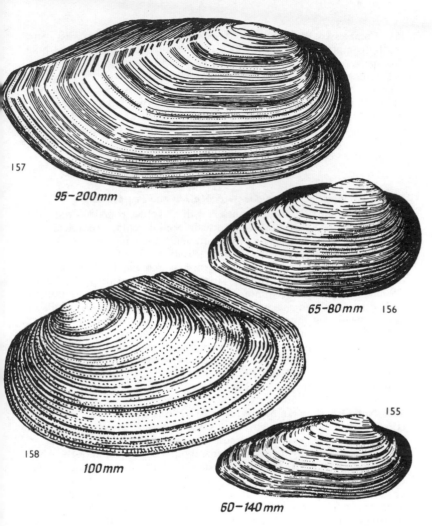

157

95-200mm

65-80mm   156

155

158

100mm

60-140mm

158. Duck Mussel: *Anodonta anatina* (L.). Shell differs from *A. cygnaea* in being smaller, markedly swollen, oval in outline, having the postero-dorsal blades more elevated, the dorsal and ventral margins widely divergent posteriorly and the lower margin more rounded. The hindmost point is well below the centre of the shell. Hinge similar to *A. cygnaea*. Variable; muscle-scar characters in key are more reliable. Colour dark greenish-grey to green-brown. L: 100 mm., H: 60 mm., B: 30 mm. Prefers hard, flowing water and a sandy bottom. Distribution: Great Britain as *A. cygnaea*, but local to the north of Scotland; local in C. Ireland; elsewhere Palaearctic.

143

159. Compressed River Mussel: *Anodonta complanata* **Rossmässler.** Shell usually compressed; outline oval, rather intermediate between the other two species as regards the degree of divergence between the dorsal and well-rounded ventral margins; straight dorsal margin shorter than in *A. cygnaea*, but development and elevation of postero-dorsal blades very variable; umbones not very swollen, further forward than in the other species; hinge as usual. For more reliable muscle-scar characters, see key. Colour dark olive-green to moss-green. L: 90 mm., H: 50 mm., B: 20–35 mm. Lives in rivers and sometimes canals, Distribution: local from Dorset and southern counties to S.E. Yorkshire; elsewhere W. Europe.

SUPERFAMILY SPHAERIACEA

Family Sphaeriidae (*Orb Mussels and Pea Mussels*)

Small to minute freshwater mussels with a swollen, rounded or angular, more or less oval shell and a numerically well-developed complement of hinge-teeth (a_{i-iii}, c_{2-4}, p_{i-iii}). The umbones are more or less anterior (*Sphaerium*) or more or less posterior (*Pisidium*). The foot is long (longer than the shell in some species), worm-like and highly extensible. The mantle is produced into 2 long siphons (*Sphaerium*) or 1 shorter one (*Pisidium*), the inhalant siphon being the longer and smaller-mouthed in each case. The young may be attached by a byssus, but the adults are always free-living mud- or sand-dwellers. We have 4 British species of *Sphaerium* and 16 of *Pisidium*, making 20 representatives in all of this large and difficult family. Much work remains to be done on the causes of variation within species and on the factors which determine distribution. The brief notes below should be supplemented by reference to the additional information contained in the key.

160. Nut Orb Mussel: *Sphaerium* (*S.*) *rivicola* (**Lamarck**). Our largest species. Shell large, swollen, thick-walled; outline broadly elliptical to transversely oval; umbones almost central, small, broadly arched and slightly elevated, merging into the general outline, except anteriorly, where, being tipped forward, they have a steeper slope; hinge-ligament visible externally; strongest teeth c_2, a_{i-ii}, p_{i-ii}; surface glossy, striated in the upper third (lens) then concentrically ribbed; colour yellowish or reddish horn-brown to olive. L: 18–24 mm. (exceptionally 27 mm.), H: 15–18 mm., B: 10–14 mm. Lives in slow rivers and canals. Distribution: Exeter Canal to Yorkshire, also Northumberland, Brecon, Montgomery; elsewhere C. Europe.

161. Horny Orb Mussel: *Sphaerium* (*S.*) *corneum* (**L.**). Our commonest species. Shell small to medium-sized, swollen, thin-walled; outline broadly oval, almost equilateral; umbones broadly arched, weakly elevated, barely breaking the general profile, but slightly tipped forwards; short hinge-ligament almost concealed externally; hinge-plate fairly strong; strongest teeth a_{i-ii}, p_{i-ii}; surface with a silky lustre and fine irregular striations (lens); yellowish horn-colour, grey or brown, with alternating light and

144

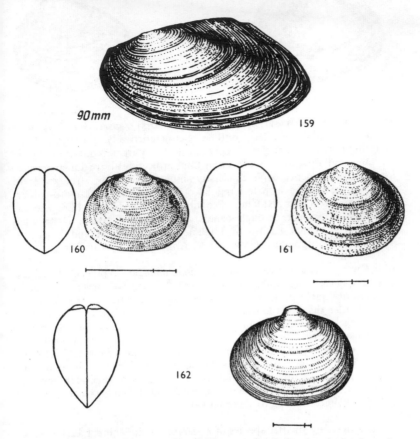

90mm

159

160

161

162

dark zones. L: 10–14 mm., H: 7–10 mm., B: 7–9 mm. Animal prefers clean, moving water in rivers, canals and large drainage-ditches. Distribution: British Isles, general; elsewhere Holarctic.

162. Lake Orb Mussel: *Sphaerium (Musculium) lacustre* (Müller). Shell small, compressed, very thin-walled and fragile; outline rounded trapezoidal to transversely oval; umbones conical, inclined forwards, elevated high above the general profile and very characteristically capped by the embryonal shell (nepionic shell, prodissoconch); short hinge-ligament concealed externally; hinge-plate weak; strongest teeth a_{ii}, p_{ii}; surface silky or glossy with faint regular striations (lens); colour grey-white to yellowish-white, often with dark zones and a pale edge. L: 8–10 mm. (to 15 mm. under favourable conditions), H: 7–8 mm., B: 4–4·5 mm. Animal lives more in ponds and ditches than in running water, often under conditions tolerated by few other species. Distribution: general in England and Wales, Scotland north to Perth (also Ross), E. and S.E. Ireland; elsewhere Palaearctic.

163

164

163. Oblong Orb Mussel: *Sphaerium* (*Musculium*) *transversum* **(Say).** Shell medium-sized, thin-walled; outline characteristically rounded-oblong, anterior part semicircular, longer posterior part a rounded square; umbones well forward, broadly arched but projecting above dorsal margin; long hinge-ligament visible externally; hinge-plate weak; strongest teeth a_{i-iii}, p_{i-iii}; surface with fine regular striations (lens); pale horn-colour. L: 13 mm., H: 9 mm., B: 6 mm. Probably introduced about 1830, and has since spread widely through canals and canalised rivers. Distributed through the "canal basin" of England from Somerset and Surrey to Yorkshire, Montgomery; elsewhere N. America (not yet in Europe).

164. River (or Giant) Pea Mussel: *Pisidium amnicum* **(Müller).** The largest British species. Shell thick-walled, swollen; outline transversely oval to rounded-obliquely-triangular; umbones broad, situated at the beginning of the hinder third of the shell and projecting widely above the shell-outline; hinge-plate strong and broad (generic character); hinge-tooth c_3 forked; surface glossy with strong, irregular concentric striations (lens); colour yellow-grey to grey-brown with a paler marginal zone. L: 8–11 mm., H: 5–8·5 mm., B: 4–6 mm. Lives in fine sand or mud in clean, hard, flowing water in rivers, streams, canals and lakes. Distribution: general in England, N., E., S.E. and S.W. Wales, E. and C. Scotland, Ireland, except N.W. and S.W.; elsewhere Europe to Lake Baikal.

The remaining smaller species of *Pisidium* are difficult subjects even for an expert; their shells require careful preparation and examination with a low-powered binocular microscope, and their adequate description and illustration calls for far more space than we have available in this book. The key on pages 137–140 represents the best possible short guide to identification, and in borrowing it from Ellis (1962) we have done our best to simplify the technical terms and to add a few notes on distribution where these afford clues to the inclusion or exclusion of species. Young specialists who wish to pursue the genus further should obtain Ellis's *Synopsis* with the confidence that this is the best and most lavishly illustrated modern account, and that the present book has provided them with the necessary foundations to understand it. A check-list of the remaining British species follows:

165. Caserta Pea Mussel: *P. casertanum* **(Poli).**
166. Arctic-alpine Pea Mussel: *P. conventum* **Clessin.**
167. Henslow's Pea Mussel: *P. henslowanum* **(Sheppard).**

146

168. **Globular Pea Mussel:** *P. hibernicum* Westerlund.
169. **Lilljeborg's Pea Mussel:** *P. lilljeborgii* Clessin.
170. **Quadrangular Pea Mussel:** *P. milium* Held.
171. **Pygmy Pea Mussel:** *P. moitessierianum* Paladilhe.
172. **Shining Pea Mussel:** *P. nitidum* Jenyns.
173. **Porous-shelled Pea Mussel:** *P. obtusale* (Lamarck).
174. **Red-crusted Pea Mussel:** *P. personatum* Malm.
175. **False Orb Pea Mussel:** *P. pseudosphaerium* (Favre) Altena.
176. **Iridescent Pea Mussel:** *P. pulchellum* Jenyns.
177. **Short-ended Pea Mussel:** *P. subtruncatum* Malm.
178. **Hump-backed Pea Mussel:** *P. supinum* Schmidt.
179. **Fine-lined Pea Mussel:** *P. tenuilineatum* Stelfox.

A few words on distribution may serve to illustrate the fascination which
Pisidium spp. have in store for those prepared to brave their taxonomic
difficulties. All our species are widely distributed elsewhere, being either
Holarctic (N. American, European and N. Asian) or Palaearctic (European
and N. Asian only). These wide ranges may be explained by the fact that
long before man assisted their dissemination by cutting canals from one
river system to another and inadvertently transporting molluscs on the
outsides of ships and in ballast-water, these animals were stealing rides
attached to the webbed feet of water-fowl and the legs of water-beetles
(*Dytiscus*) and water-bugs. Assisted immigration can introduce species
from far-distant regions, as we have already seen in the case of the Nearctic
(N. American) *Sphaerium transversum*; on the other hand, it is probably
nothing more than lack of transport that has kept *P. supinum* and *P.
tenuilineatum* out of Ireland.

Within the British Isles, however, the distribution-maps for the various
species present very differing pictures, which can be related to preferences
for various types of environmental conditions and to competition between
species. *P. casertanum*, *P. subtruncatum* and *P. hibernicum* are species
which occur almost everywhere, regardless of whether the water is hard or
soft, clear or muddy, flowing or stagnant. Others have more limited distributions, depending on various factors. With *P. conventum*, for example,
low temperatures are the principal need, for this species is an Arctic-Alpine
"relict", still pining, as it were, for the last Ice Age and accordingly restricted to the cold depths of a few lakes in the British Isles and a high
Cumberland swamp. Several of our species are indifferent to the hardness or
otherwise of the water. Others, however, insist on hard water, and are said
to be "calcicole" species (*P. amnicum*, *P. henslowanum*, *P. moitessierianum*,
P. tenuilineatum), while others again are "calcifuge" species, requiring soft
water (*P. personatum*, *P. obtusale*). It is as likely as not that the latter, like
the primitive *Margaritifera*, have been driven into such conditions through
inability to compete with more successful species elsewhere. *P. lilljeborgii*
has a dominating preference for a bottom of fine sand or silt, which takes it
into mountain lakes, regardless of most other considerations; *P. pulchellum*
and *P. supinum* require a muddy bottom, but insist on clean, moving water

to go with it; *P. amnicum* is indifferent as to bottom, but again requires clear, running water; *P. milium* likes a mud bottom and clean water without too rapid a flow, and accordingly keeps out of rivers; *P. obtusale* and *P. personatum* are creatures with perverted tastes, abhorring clean sand and clear, running water and living under stagnant, muddy conditions often too foul for other species. Yet *P. pseudosphaerium* is capriciously confined to marsh-drains in Somerset and Sussex and a marl-pit in Cheshire; perhaps a reader of this book will one day tell us why!

SUPERFAMILY DREISSENACEA

Family Dreissenidae (*Zebra Mussels*)

A small family of medium-sized freshwater mussels, reminiscent in many ways of the marine mussels (*Mytilus*). The shell is shaped like a very broad boomerang, with the umbones right at the pointed anterior end. The hinge-plate is toothless, or at best with a single rudimentary *p*, and the hinge-ligament is concealed. The edges of the mantle are fused, except for a small gap which permits the extensile, worm-like foot and the byssus (which attaches the animal to stones, etc.) to protrude. There is a large, long inhalant siphon and a shorter exhalant one. The Dreissenidae do not have a glochidium larva (page 24). Instead, they have a veliger (the form commonest in aquatic molluscs), which is a tiny ciliated larva which swims around in the water until it settles down on the bottom, secretes a little byssus from a gland in its foot, and turns into a baby zebra mussel. We have only one "British" species, which lived all over Europe some thousands of years ago until its distribution-area shrank back to S. Russia, whence, during the last 150 years, it has been spreading all over Europe again.

180. Zebra Mussel; Wandering Mussel: *Dreissena polymorpha* (Pallas). Shell medium-sized, swollen, thick-walled; outline rounded isosceles-triangular, anterior end pointed, dorsal margin sharply keeled, postero-dorsal margin bluntly keeled, hinder end well-rounded, ventral margin deeply concave; umbones situated at anterior tip; hinge-plate toothless; surface glossy, at first finely striated, becoming coarser posteriorly; colour yellowish, greyish or brownish, with alternating zig-zag or wavy bands ("zebra"). L: 25–40 mm. (exceptionally 50 mm.), H: 13–18 mm., B: 17–23 mm. Arrived in Surrey Commercial Docks, London, about 1824, probably attached to shipping from the Baltic, and had spread through most of our canals by 1840. Distribution: Exeter Canal to Yorkshire, C. Scotland; elsewhere much of Europe to the Caspian Sea.

180

Part Six

Keeping Snails and Mussels in Aquaria and Terraria

A true naturalist does not rest content with collecting and naming shells; he wants to know something about the animals' way of life. You will have little opportunity to study the lives of snails and mussels during your collecting expeditions, because most of the land-snails encountered will be in a resting condition, and in the case of aquatic species observation is often hindered by deep or turbid water. You cannot always count on finding a given species active in a particular place at a chosen convenient time, and so, if you want to study the animal's everyday life and activities, it will be necessary to keep it and observe it in captivity. (This need not involve great complication or expense.)

An Aquarium for Freshwater Snails and Mussels Snails, and to a much lesser extent mussels, are sometimes kept along with ornamental fishes in the optimistic belief that they will serve as window-cleaners and scavengers or water-filters respectively. To us, however, they are the main objects of interest and should therefore be kept by themselves. This also has the advantage that we can dispense with special aeration, since these very slow animals have no great oxygen/carbon dioxide turnover. The size of the vessel determines the size and number of the animals which can be kept in it. A 2-lb. jam-jar would be large enough for two or three small Pond Snails (*Lymnaea*) or Ram's-horn Snails (*Planorbis*). On the other hand, for a Great Ram's-horn Snail (*Planorbarius corneus*) or a Great Pond Snail (*L. stagnalis*) at least a 4-lb. jam-jar is necessary. For species requiring still larger accommodation, you will need small all-glass aquaria or suitable substitutes. A large River Snail (*Viviparus viviparus*) or two or three small mussels would require an aquarium about $12 \times 6 \times 6$ in., while several River Snails or a single large Freshwater Mussel (*Unio* or *Anodonta* sp.) would need something at least two or three times this size.

The aim must be to simulate in miniature the natural environment of the animals. Ideally, therefore, you should bring water from the place where you caught them, together with the appropriate soil in the form of gravel, sand or mud and, finally, typical water-

149

plants from the site of capture. For small vessels one suitable plant will be sufficient; for larger ones one or more specimens of several species should be provided (*see* Figure 25). Very suitable and easily procured plants include Canadian Waterweed (*Elodea canadensis*), Water Milfoil (*Myriophyllum verticillatum*), Hornwort (*Ceratophyllum demersum*), Frogbit (*Hydrocharis morsus-ranae*), Duckweed (*Lemna* spp.), Broad Pondweed (*Potamogeton natans*), Willow Moss (*Fontinalis antipyretica*), and Water Starwort (*Callitriche verna*).

The elements of a natural environment in miniature comprise as many animals as the volume of water will support, as many plants as can maintain themselves in spite of being devoured by snails, and a sufficiency of soil for the plant-roots. You will know that you have attained a biological equilibrium when you find that, apart from replacing water lost by evaporation, you have nothing to do but watch.

The technique of setting up the aquarium is simple enough. First, put in the appropriate soil and add just a couple of inches of water to support the water-plants. Then plant the plants, and not too many, because whatever may be said about the "balanced" aquarium during the daytime, at night both plants and animals are respiring and contributing to the build-up of carbon dioxide in the water. Next, add the rest of the water, taking care not to stir up the bottom so that the water is made turbid and the leaves all covered with silt. In the case of a large aquarium, stand a jar or jug on the bottom and pour the water into that so that it spills quietly over the rim. Then leave the aquarium to settle down for a few days, so that the plants can establish themselves and prepare to provide fodder for the snails. In this way, too, you can take stock of the animals which have been introduced accidentally. Sponges, *Tubifex* and other worms, freshwater polyps, and water-fleas and other crustacea are welcome guests; not so welcome are species which will prey on the snails, such as leeches, dragonfly larvae and larvae of the carnivorous water-beetle, *Dytiscus marginalis*. Being satisfied that all is in order, you can then add the species you wish to observe.

Finally (and in the case of a large tank, before now), select a suitable position for the aquarium, where it will, at least for part of the day, receive adequate lighting for plant-growth. Intense sunlight should, however, be avoided, because, apart from the lighting preferences of the animals, there can be serious consequences when the temperature of the water becomes too high.

It should be emphasised that the larger freshwater mussels present

Figure 25. Aquarium plants: (*a*) Ivy-leaved Duckweed (*Lemna trisulca*), (*b*) Lesser Duckweed (*L. minor*), (*c*) Willow Moss, (*d*) Water Milfoil, (*e*) Canadian Waterweed, (*f*) Hornwort, (*g*) Frogbit, (*h*) Broad Pondweed. (*See* page 150.)

a serious problem in captivity. They are filter-feeders, depending on micro-organisms and other food-particles which they strain out of the water through their gills. In a typical case, a large *Unio* or *Anodonta* will filter the water of a fair-sized tank crystal-clear in twenty-four hours, and then slowly starve, die and eventually transform the whole aquarium into a stinking horror. Apart from using a very large, well-established aquarium with a sufficient production of micro-fauna to keep pace with the mussel's food-demands, there is little that can be done; adding water from other rich tanks or from a suitable river or pond is a remedy which will soon weary even the most enthusiastic naturalist.

The Terrarium It is desirable to provide captive animals with conditions which approximate as closely as possible to those of the natural habitat of the species in question. As we have seen, this is relatively easy to achieve in the case of aquatic species in an aquarium. On the other hand, terrestrial species in a terrarium present rather greater difficulties, since here we become responsible for regulating a whole complex of living conditions, including humidity, food-supply, sanitation and general biological equilibrium. However, the necessary measures are quite quickly executed leaving ample time for observation.

Land animals, just like aquatic ones, have certain minimum space requirements which must be satisfied if they are to be kept under natural conditions. The largest species, such as the Roman Snail (*Helix pomatia*) or the Great Black Slug (*Arion ater*), require about 120 cu. in. for each individual animal. Relatively large snails, such as the Banded Snails (*Cepaea* spp.) and the Bush Snail (*Fruticicola fruticum*), and medium-sized slugs need 30 cu. in. each. Medium-sized snails, like the larger Hairy Snails (*Trichia* spp.) and species of *Helicella*, need 15 cu. in. apiece, while 8 cu. in. will do for one to several specimens of the smallest species, according to size. These indications will serve as a rough guide in planning our arrangements.

The character of the terrarium requires consideration as well as the size. Most of our prospective tenants require plenty of air, light and moisture, and we should therefore avoid keeping them in all-glass receptacles for any length of time. Small, lacquered insectaria which, apart from a solid base and one glass wall, are surrounded by wire gauze on all sides (Figure 26) can be purchased ready-made and are very suitable for our purpose; those who object to paying fancy prices should have little difficulty in copying the design themselves in wood, glass and perforated zinc. Several holes should be bored in the bottom to allow surplus water to drain away

Figure 26. A terrarium.

(and something provided to catch the drips if the terrarium is kept indoors), because stagnant moisture is bad for snails and inimical to the simulation of natural conditions. Directly on the bottom, put a layer of very coarse gravel, which can be mixed with stone-chippings, rubble, etc.; this will serve as a subsoil and further drainage. Next to this comes a layer of loose earth mixed with pieces of chalk. The thickness of this topsoil depends on the size of the species to be kept; large species require about 4 in., so that they can dig in and later lay their eggs. Finally, upon the earth, lay a cushion of moss, a piece of turf, a few stones, and some leaf-mould or rotten wood, according to the species you intend to keep. Restrain yourself from being over-generous with these furnishings; you want to see something of the animals! There should always, however, be a little nook with moss, since this, by its sponginess, helps to preserve a certain residual humidity. Among non-molluscan tenants, an earthworm may be recommended, since this will help to keep the soil loose.

It is not absolutely essential to plant any further herbs in the terrarium, since these are already represented in the turf. But you may do so, provided you select plants which are not exactly the favourite food of the snails you are keeping; here experience is the best guide to policy. As long as there is regular supplementary

153

feeding, snails generally treat the following species with respect: Moneywort or Creeping Jenny (*Lysimachia nummularia*), Water Avens (*Geum rivale*), Ground Ivy (*Nepeta* or *Glechoma hederacea*), Tansy (*Tanecetum vulgare*), Ivy (*Hedera helix*), Daisy (*Bellis perennis*) (Figure 27). Contrariwise, once you have ascertained the food-preferences of the snails, you can, if you wish, plant only the preferred plants, and spare yourself much of the labour of regular feeding. In this case it will only be necessary to renew the plants when their growth fails to keep pace with the animals' appetites.

And how else can the snails be fed? Even though all species do not eat alike, as future researches will clearly show, it is still possible to draw up a menu whose composition will satisfy a great many of our native snails. Dandelion (*Taraxacum officinale*), Stinging Nettles (*Urtica* spp.), lettuce, spinach, beans, sliced potatoes, carrots and turnips head the list—always raw, of course. Sliced cucumbers, pumpkins, bananas, fresh fruits and tomatoes are gladly taken, and flour paste and softened bread are also well received. Make it a habit always to offer only two or three morsels at a time, and not too much of these. The animals are no gluttons, most of them can be destroyed within a short time, and all food-remains endanger the cleanliness of the terrarium.

Cleanliness is the factor by which the biological equilibrium of this small microcosm of Nature stands or falls. Upon it depends the well-being and natural behaviour of the animals. Take care, therefore, to remove all food-remains before they go mouldy or begin to ferment, and likewise, at intervals of a few days, cleanse the terrarium of all accumulated excrement and slime from the snails. Furthermore, renew the cushion of moss every week, and once a month clean out the whole terrarium and replace the old soil with new. The animals in such a well-tended terrarium will enjoy health and normal life—and that is to your advantage as well as theirs.

It is well known that humidity is a very important environmental factor for slugs and snails. If you leave the water-economy of the terrarium to itself, you will not see much of the animals; they will either creep away somewhere or cling, withdrawn into their shells, to the walls. Since they take no food in this condition, many of them will sooner or later die. This can be prevented by sprinkling the whole terrarium with water sufficiently frequently to be sure that the humidity is always high enough. The life and activity of the snails will soon indicate the correct amount. If the subsoil and drainage-holes have been properly arranged, surplus water will, in any case, run away through the holes in the bottom.

In addition to the high proportion of species which like a certain

Figure 27. Plants for the terrarium, a Moneywort or Creeping
Jenny, b Water Avens, c Ground Ivy, d Tansy, e Ivy, f Daisy.
(*See* page 154.)

humidity, there are also a few in our fauna, such as the *Helicella* spp. and others, which prefer warmth and dryness. Such species naturally require to be accommodated in a special terrarium which is sprinkled less frequently, and consequently needs no drainage. This terrarium should also stand in the sun for a short while each day, a condition to be avoided if possible in the case of moist terraria. Light and air must have continual access to all terraria, however, and, furthermore, when they are kept outdoors they must be adequately protected against rain; a good shower provides too much water for the thin layers of earth.

Part Seven

Observation and Research

With well-kept snails, slugs and mussels installed in terraria and aquaria, a new field of malacology (the science of molluscs) opens up; observation of, and research into, their ways of life. You are not likely to discover any new species in this country, apart from the chance of finding an exotic species which has been introduced as a greenhouse escape, etc., but you may still hope to make many discoveries which will be material contributions to molluscan biology. The whole complex web of life is open to investigation and, even if you find the possibilities seemingly exhausted in the case of a few species, there will be comparable studies still to be carried out on many others. The following pages provide a first introduction to biological researches, classified according to the animals' various vital activities, from which anyone with patience and some gift for observation can soon expect to achieve results.

Locomotion

It is an accurate enough statement to say that "a snail creeps" or "a mussel creeps", but it explains very little biologically. Many animals creep, but by different ways and means in various groups. How different, for example, is the creeping of a snake from that of an earthworm! Exactly how, then, is the creeping of snails, slugs and mussels accomplished?

Let us first of all take a look at the snails. They glide quietly and steadily along the ground and, with the clearest possible view, we cannot see just what happens. Perhaps a look underneath a snail will help? Put a snail in a Petri dish or other dish with a flat glass bottom and look at the creeping sole of the foot from underneath. This seems to lie quite smoothly against the glass and to push itself as a whole over the surface. But if you look more carefully, perhaps with a hand-lens, you will see that there is movement going on within the sole itself. There are "waves" running from behind forwards or *vice versa* which push the sole forwards, and with it the animal. These waves are muscular contractions; they do not appear in the resting animal. The short intervals (wavelengths) between the waves as they succeed one another are responsible for the steadiness of the snail's body as it glides along.

Another observation can be made in this connection. The snail leaves a glistening track behind it which is at first sticky and then stiffens. This is mucus (slime) which is secreted by glands at the anterior end of the creeping sole. So a snail never moves directly over a surface, but upon its own band of slime, a continuously extending "carpet" of its own making! This is most impressively demonstrated by letting the animal creep over a razor blade; it will take not the slightest harm from the sharp edge.

And how do water-snails manage? They, too, have the same mode of locomotion, insert a similar slime-band between the creeping sole and the substrate, and have the same steady snail-tempo as their terrestrial relatives. They have a further aptitude which belongs to them alone: they can creep along the underside of the water surface. How do they do that? Here again they secrete a mucus-band which holds so firmly to the surface-film of the water (which is under tension) that the snails can hang from it.

Careful study of various species of snails while they are creeping, makes it possible to establish regular distinctions in tempo. Snail tempo is to an astonishing degree characteristic of the individual species. It may perhaps amuse you to measure the speeds of various species and express this in miles per hour! Well, here is a tip: Snails proper can best be brought out of their shells and induced to creep by a bath in lukewarm water, while motionless slugs can be persuaded to move across a glass surface if you warm the glass beneath them by rubbing. Lazy snails can also be brought to a "fast trot" in the same way.

Understanding the locomotion of mussels requires a great deal more patience, yet the process is so peculiar and unique that the hours necessary to study it may be well worth while. Mussels certainly have a so-called "foot", yet it is neither walking nor creeping that they do. The foot is protruded anteriorly, down between the valves of the shell, and at the same time distended by being filled with blood. In the River Mussels (Unionidae) it is then driven deep into the soil and fastened by the swelling of the anterior, buried end. Once this anchoring has been accomplished the rest of the foot contracts and shortens so that the mussel is pulled along after it, and as the whole cycle is repeated the animal ploughs its way along the bottom. The Orb Mussels (Sphaeriidae) and Zebra Mussels (Dreissenidae) have fundamentally the same mode of locomotion, but in these cases anchoring of the foot is not achieved by boring and swelling; here the protruded foot is attached to the substrate by means of mucus, a faculty which is probably both permitted and demanded by the animal's smaller size.

Feeding

How do snails eat? Here, above all, lies a broad field for investigation and research. Information is most easily and naturally obtained by paying attention to food-plants in the field during collecting excursions. Among other things, you will learn that certain slugs specialise in eating fungi, and that others feed on excrement or carrion. You will observe further that, among the plant-eaters, some choose fresh and others faded plant-parts.

Once you have achieved a basic knowledge of the feeding habits of a few or many species of snails and slugs by such methods, you can design experiments in order to obtain more precise knowledge. For this purpose, bring home 10–20 specimens of the species you wish to investigate and put them, together with one plant species from their natural environment, in a small terrarium which otherwise contains nothing else but earth. Then, every twenty-four hours, change the plant species. On one occasion provide a living plant rooted in the soil, on the next a withering plant of the same species, so that you can immediately decide the preferred condition of the food-plant. Before making each change first note the extent of the food devoured, on the lines: not eaten/only nibbled/eaten/ largely eaten/plant wholly devoured. In addition, record whether certain parts of the food-plant are preferred, and whether predominantly fresh or withered material is eaten. Pay attention, too, to the effect that any known defensive structures of the plant— stinging hairs, thorns, latex, etc.—have upon the snails' feeding. Having discovered a number of acceptable food-plants, try presenting them two at a time, noting which is preferred on each occasion, so that you can list the species in order of preference. Finally, consider the question whether specialised feeding on higher plants merely involves grazing on fungi or algae growing on (epiphytic on) the plant substrate or on rotting plants.

Thus in our investigations into feeding, as in scientific research generally, the answer to every question poses further problems for solution.

It should also be mentioned that important additional information concerning certain food-materials may be obtained by teasing small pieces of mollusc excrement in a drop of water on a glass slide and examining them under a microscope.

You can proceed in a basically similar manner with water-snails, even though these involve further difficulties. However, water-snails grazing on the algae growing on the glass sides of an aquarium may provide us with a useful answer to another question: *How* do snails feed? We know that they possess a rasping tongue, the radula, supported by a "cartilage" and operated by muscles. This movable structure works in opposition to a fixed, horny jaw in the roof of the mouth. Viewing the mouth-parts of a grazing snail through a lens you can see how it presses its mouth against the glass pane, opens its lips, and lets the radula glide over the algal film. You may also see how it cuts a swathe through the algae in its path. The devouring process in a land-snail can be studied in a similar fashion by letting it feed on a glass plate on which you have smeared a thin film of flour and water. Though you certainly cannot see very much happening when a large land-snail is feeding on a plant, you may be able to hear the rasping noise made by the mouth-parts as it bites off small pieces. The food is then swallowed without any further reduction in size (comminution).

Mussels, as we have already seen, are filter-feeders. The beating of innumerable microscopic, hair-like structures, or cilia, on the gills sets up a water-current, which serves both for the purposes of respiration and feeding. Tiny food-particles become entangled in mucus on the gills and carried, still by ciliary action, towards the labial palps and eventually the mouth. The gross respiratory-feeding current can be demonstrated by ejecting a drop of indian ink through a pipette opposite the inhalant opening of a large mussel and waiting to see the dark cloud emerge from the exhalant opening.

Respiration

The process of respiration is most easily observed in land-snails. The condition of the pneumostome (opening of the respiratory chamber)—wide, scarcely open or closed—shows how matters stand with regard to breathing. Yet the extent of the gaseous exchange between the respiratory chamber and the outside atmosphere does not only depend on the size of the pneumostome, since the surrounding mantle musculature determines the filling and emptying of the respiratory cavity. Observe the condition of the pneumostome in various slugs and snails in motion and in repose. How often is the pneumostome opened and closed? Is its behaviour in resting animals different from that in creeping ones?

Respiration in gilled snails proceeds, as in other gill-breathing animals, by the uptake of oxygen dissolved in the water into the blood with the simultaneous release of carbon dioxide. Here there is something to be observed only in the Valve Snails (Valvatidae), which protrude their feathery gill into the water (Figure 22).

The breathing-relations of aquatic lunged-snails, on the other hand, are more complicated. First bring together for comparison large specimens of the Great Pond Snail (*Lymnaea stagnalis*) and the Great Ram's-horn Snail (*Planorbarius corneus*). Both these species come to the surface to renew the air in their respiratory cavities. Observe this process, and count the number of times the animals surface during a reasonable period. In this way it can be established that the *Lymnaea* needs to renew its breathing air far more frequently than the *Planorbarius*. In water rich in oxygen, the *Planorbarius* seldom comes to the surface at all. How are these observations to be interpreted?

In the first place, the *Planorbarius* has a respiratory pigment, haemoglobin, in its blood, which enables more efficient utilisation of the air breathed by the chemical binding of the oxygen. (Haemoglobin, an iron-based pigment like our own, is rare among molluscs; the usual respiratory pigment is haemocyanin, which is based on copper.) Thus at a water temperature of 15° C. (59° F.) the *Planorbarius* first rises to the surface when only 4% oxygen remains in the respiratory chamber; under the same conditions the *Lymnaea* must surface when the oxygen-content is still as high as 13%. In the second place, the *Planorbarius* possesses a kind of false "gill" on the left side (Figure 28), a lobe of skin which is richly provided with blood and always projects. This pseudo-gill is most noticeably expanded when the oxygen-tension (content) of the water is low, as during warm weather or when the water contains a lot of decomposing organic matter. In the third place, the respiratory chamber containing the "lung" is considerably larger in the *Planorbarius*.

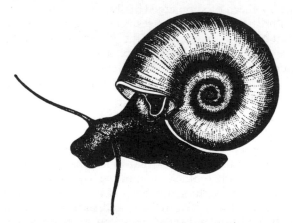

Figure 28. Great Ram's-horn Snail, *Planorbarius corneus* (living animal). Note pseudo-gill (inferior pallial lobe) on the left side below the mouth of the shell.

Figure 29. Great Pond Snail, *Lymnaea stagnalis* (living animal).

There are, however, situations in which atmospheric air is denied to aquatic lunged-snails—for example, in winter, when ice covers the water, when they wander into greater depths or, as in the case of *Lymnaea abyssalis*, live there permanently. Most *Lymnaea* spp. then carry on cutaneous respiration (breathing through the skin), in which the strongly expanded and ciliated cephalic tentacles play a considerable role (Figure 29). The small species of the family Planorbidae, which have no pseudo-gills, fill their respiratory chambers with water so that their "lungs" function as gills. The same happens in *L. abyssalis* certainly and probably in other *Lymnaea* spp., but the point is still undecided in *Planorbarius*. In the remaining Planorbidae it is easy to see whether the respiratory chamber is filled with air or with water by looking for the characteristic silvery sheen of submerged air-bubbles.

Mussels breathe by gills. The respiratory current enters through the inhalant opening, passes along the gills where gaseous exchange takes place, and leaves through the exhalant opening further laden with excreta from the gut and kidney. An experiment to demonstrate this current has already been described in the section on feeding (*see* page 160).

The Senses

Light-perception. We know that snails have simple eyes, which in the Prosobranchiata and Basommatophora lie at the bases of the single pair of cephalic tentacles and in the Stylommatophora at the tips of the posterior cephalic tentacles (Figure 18). With these eyes snails can distinguish between light and darkness and determine direction. In addition, however, they can make some simple discrimination of form. We can demonstrate this faculty by bringing a number of Banded Snails (*Cepaea nemoralis* or *C. hortensis*) into a

162

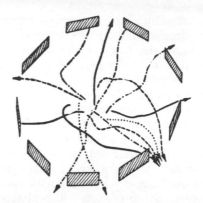

Figure 30. Arrangement of an experiment to demonstrate perception of form in snails (for explanation see text). After von Buddenbrock.

polygonal enclosure in which "walls" and "gangways" alternate with one another (Figure 30). Since the snails creep to the edges of the dividing walls, they will almost all find an opening at the first attempt. This behaviour is the more striking in that snails given simple light stimuli almost always avoid the light. In our experiment, however, they creep past the darker obstacles towards the light, guided by their recognition of shapes.

It often happens that when we make movements in the vicinity of a creeping snail the animal halts and begins to retract its tentacles and head. If we have not disturbed or jolted it, this behaviour can only be a reaction to shadowing. This can be tested by suddenly shading a creeping snail with the flat of the hand. This shadow-reflex is no doubt an adaptation useful as a defensive reaction to a possible enemy. The diffused light-sensitivity of the skin, particularly that of the anterior part of the body at the edge of the shell, is pre-eminently important in regard to this shadow-reflex.

Similar shadow-reflexes are displayed by mussels, in which also there is an illumination-reflex which prevents them from protruding their elongated inhalant and exhalant siphons too far out of the soil.

Chemical-perception. Under this designation we include the senses of smell and taste, since a cut-and-dried distinction between them is seldom possible. The main centres of chemo-sensitivity are the cephalic tentacles, the lips and the edge of the foot, especially the anterior end of the last. This can be tested by placing a drop of sugar-solution in the path of a creeping snail; as soon as the edge of the sole touches the drop the animal halts and begins sucking up the sugar. A corresponding solution of saccharine is avoided, likewise a 1% quinine solution. A *Lymnaea* creeping under the

163

surface-film displays corresponding reactions when the solutions are dropped directly on to the opening of the mouth.

Snails also react to stimulation by distant scents, a process comparable to scent-perception in higher animals. Among slugs fungus-eaters start moving towards preferred species from up to 20 in. away, and the Roman Snail (*Helix pomatia*) and its relatives will creep slightly smaller distances towards plucked lettuces, dandelions and other favourite foods. The site of this chemo-reception is still unknown, but, although special sense-organs have not yet been detected, it seems likely to be in the cephalic tentacles. If streaks of various chemicals (ammonia, bromine, sulphuric acid) are drawn across a snail's path and the behaviour of the tentacles is carefully noted, you will probably come to the same conclusion.

In the Prosobranchiata there is a special organ of chemo-reception, the osphradium, a gill-like structure in the gill chamber, which is apparently concerned with sampling the respiratory water.

In mussels chemo-sensitivity is especially strongly displayed at the edge of the mantle and at the inhalant and exhalant openings.

Mechanical sense. In snails the whole outer skin is sensitive to touch; this is easily demonstrated in any species. At stronger stimuli snails withdraw into their shells and slugs shorten their bodies to a fraction of the normal length. At the same time the latter secrete slime in quite considerable quantities, a useful protection against being seized by an enemy.

In mussels the inhalant opening and its surroundings are particularly sensitive to touch. Here very often there are wart-like sensory papillae which detect coarse particles and prevent them entering the inhalant stream into the respiratory chamber.

Reproduction

Reproduction in snails begins with pairing. This process is best observed in a land-snail; the Roman Snail (*Helix pomatia*) is an especially suitable subject. In early summer these hermaphrodite animals may be found engaging in a preliminary love-play. A pair of them raise their creeping soles off the ground and bring them together, while at the same time they rock their bodies to and fro and actively caress one another with their greatly extended cephalic tentacles (Figure 31). After a short time the love-play passes into a love-duel; each snail projects its calcareous love-dart into the sole of the partner (Figures 5, 32). Thereupon the two animals become interlocked, and often remain thus for a long time, until they once more raise themselves and the actual mating occurs, during which

Figure 31. Courtship of the Roman Snail (*Helix pomatia*).

each everts its penis and ejects the fertilising sperm into the vagina of the partner. The two snails then separate, and each stores the sperm of the other until its own eggs have ripened.

About four to six weeks later the eggs are ripe and are fertilised (*see* page 19). About this time—it is now high summer—the shells of the Roman Snail are often found lying about with their openings pressed to the ground. If you try to collect such a specimen you will encounter a powerful resistance. The shell is not empty, in fact, and the body of the living occupant is extended deep into the soil. Here the animal has dug a pit in which it has deposited its eggs (Figure 33). There are, in fact, some 30 to 50 eggs, each with a white, calcareous shell. After laying, the snail closes the hole again with earth and leaves the eggs to themselves. Burying protects the eggs from predators and at the same time ensures that they have sufficient moisture for their subsequent development; it is for this reason that frequent hoeing is such a good method of controlling slugs and snails in the garden.

Courtship behaviour-patterns vary in different species, and there is still a great deal to be learned about them. The story of the Roman Snail may seem bizarre enough, but the Great Grey Slug (*Limax maximus*) actually mates in mid-air while both partners are suspended by a stout thread of mucus from a branch of a tree!

Try to observe the pairing behaviour and egg-laying of various species of snails and slugs in the terrarium. Note all your observations

Figure 32. Love-dart of a Roman Snail (magnified) and a transverse section through the same.

Figure 33. Roman Snail laying its eggs.

165

in day-books, recording accurate data on the behaviour-patterns with their durations and dates. Count the clutches of eggs, and note the size of the eggs, their colour and the nature of their shells. After the animals have mated, isolate them for this purpose in individual small containers provided with at least a 2-in. layer of earth.

Water-snails do not usually lay their eggs singly, but deposit them in gelatinous bands or plates on a firm substrate (Figure 34). You will often see such egg-masses on the glass sides of the aquarium. But if you keep only River-snails (Viviparidae), you may be surprised to find little snails coming to the surface without your having

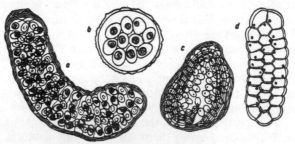

Figure 34. Spawn (magnified) of various species of water-snails. a Ear Pond Snail (*Lymnaea auricularia*), b Lake Limpet (*Acroloxus lacustris*), c Great Ram's-horn Snail (*Planorbarius corneus*), d Common Bithynia (*Bithynia tentaculata*). After Wesenberg-Lund.

noticed any spawn previously. The snails of this family are, in fact, viviparous (live-bearing), as their name indicates, and the eggs complete their development within the uterus of the mother.

In the mussels there is no pairing, and the sperm is disseminated from one animal to another through the respiratory streams (*see* page 24).

Development

If you have succeeded in inducing land-snails or slugs to lay, you must look after the eggs, for the conditions in the small glass in which they were deposited do not correspond to those in Nature, especially as regards humidity and aeration. It is best to completely dispense with soil and put the eggs on moist wadding or moss in a box of some artificial material, having numerous fine perforations in the cover and bottom. During the daily examination to see that there is sufficient moisture (but no free liquid) the process of development can be examined through a strong lens. During the greater part of the developmental period you will perceive only insignificant changes, such as, for example, an increase in the volume of the eggs after laying or a change in transparency. Later, however, the colouring in most species changes to brownish, caused by the outer membrane of the embryonal shell, and soon the tiny snails emerge from the egg-case.

Many questions concerning the developmental process can be answered by your own direct observations. How long does development last in individual species? How great are the distinctions? How are they to be interpreted? What effect does a higher or lower temperature have? How high is the hatching-rate? Note all this information and, in addition, write descriptions of the young (colour, size, number of whorls in the embryonal shell, behaviour, etc.). If you find eggs of an unidentified species in the wild, bring them home and rear the young until you can determine them.

Spawning water-snails is easier, since the aquarium provides natural conditions. All you have to do is to observe, though you may with advantage detach a mass of spawn and transfer it to a watch-glass of water, taking care that it does not dry up. In this way you can see much more of the process of development than in land-snails' eggs, and can at pleasure view them as transparent objects or by dark-ground illumination. Development is also more rapid in water-snails' eggs, because environmental conditions are more constant. Now, if you have a low-power microscope at your disposal, you may see daily, and towards the end of development almost hourly, something new: growth, movements, circulation and hatching, to name only a few. Once you understand the normal process of things and have recorded everything in writing, you can then set about changing the environmental conditions (e.g. water temperature, pH, lime- and salt-content of the water) and see what effects these changes have.

Bibliography

CHAPTER 1. (General structure of Molluscs)

The Invertebrata, by L. A. Borradaile, F. A. Potts, L. E. S. Eastham and J. T. Saunders. Third Edition, revised by G. A. Kerkut (1958). Cambridge University Press. £2 15s.

A good general introduction and a conservative classification, presented in a standard modern university textbook.

Molluscs, by J. E. Morton (1958). Hutchinson's University Library. 10s. 6d.

Covers the general structure, evolution and classification of molluscs, with chapters on the various organ-systems and a very advanced classification of the lamellibranchs.

Articles in the *Encyclopaedia Britannica* and *Chambers' Encyclopaedia*.

"*Shells Take You Over World Horizons*", by R. Platt (1949). *National Geographic Magazine*, Vol. XCVI, No. 1, pages 33–84. Out of print; second-hand, 6d. to 2s.

Includes 32 pages of coloured plates illustrating many hundreds of shells, including many of the interesting tree-dwelling snails of Florida, Cuba and the Philippine Islands.

CHAPTER 2. (Forming a collection of Molluscs)

The Preservation of Natural History Specimens, Vol. 1. *Invertebrates*, by R. Wagstaffe and J. H. Fidler (1957). H. F. and G. Witherby. £2 2s.

Instructions for Collectors, No. 9a. *Invertebrate Animals Other than Insects*. British Museum (Natural History), Cromwell Road, London, S.W.7. 3s. 6d., plus postage.

Shells, by R. Cameron (1961). Weidenfeld and Nicolson (Pleasures and Treasures Series). £1 7s. 6d.

A book mainly concerned with the aesthetic approach to sea-shells, here recommended for its lavishly illustrated accounts of the history of shell-collecting and of fine old illustrated books on shells.

CHAPTER 3. (Principles of classification and taxonomy)

The Classification of Animals: an Introduction to Zoological Taxonomy, by W. T. Calman (1949). Methuen (*Monographs on Biological Subjects*). 10s. 6d.

Animal Species and Their Evolution, by A. J. Cain (1954). Hutchinson's University Library. 8s. 6d.

168

CHAPTERS 4 and 5. (British Land and Freshwater Molluscs)

Shell Life, by E. Step, revised by W. J. Stokoe (1945). Warne (Wayside and Woodland Series). 15*s*.

The only nearly complete modern account of the British land, freshwater and marine molluscs in print has been reprinted for too many years with too little revision, but remains useful for its coloured and other illustrations of hundreds of species and a great deal of good old-fashioned natural history.

British Snails, by A. E. Ellis (1926). Oxford University Press. Out of print and scarce; a second-hand copy would be well worth having.

A book which has obviously been overtaken by changes in nomenclature and new discoveries, but which nevertheless wears its years with grace. Covers land and freshwater snails and slugs with descriptions of all the living and subfossil species then known and many of the named varieties; photographic illustrations usually provide three views of each typical form, together with further figures of many of the varieties. The best account of the British Pulmonata, and still useful as a supplement to the works by Quick and by Graham and Fretter.

A Key to the British Fresh- and Brackish-water Gastropods, by T. T. Macan (1960). Freshwater Biological Association, The Ferry House, Far Sawrey, Ambleside, Westmorland. 3*s*., postage 4*d*.

British Prosobranch Molluscs, by V. Fretter and A. Graham (1962). Bernard Quaritch (Ray Society Monographs). £8 8*s*.

A comprehensive and magnificently illustrated study of all aspects of these animals by two distinguished specialists. (Membership of the Ray Society costs £2 2*s*. per annum, which covers a copy of the monograph on some group of British animals or plants published by the Society every year and the opportunity to buy earlier monographs still in stock at greatly reduced prices. Apply to The Hon. Secretary, The Ray Society, c/o British Museum (Natural History), Cromwell Road, London, S.W.7.)

The Slugs in Our Gardens, by H. F. Barnes (1949). *New Biology*, No. 6. Penguin Books. Out of print; second-hand, 6*d*. to 1*s*.

Includes illustrations of all the species.

British Slugs (*Pulmonata; Testacellidae, Arionidae, Limacidae*), by H. E. Quick (1960). *Bulletin of the British Museum* (*Natural History*) *Zoology*, Vol. 6, No. 3. B.M. (N.H.), Cromwell Road, London, S.W.7. £2 5*s*., plus postage.

The fullest modern work, with illustrations and anatomical figures.

Slugs, by. H. E. Quick (1949). (*Synopses of the British Fauna*, No. 8). Linnean Society of London, Burlington House, Piccadilly, London, W.1. 5*s*., plus postage.

British Freshwater Bivalve Molluscs, by A. E. Ellis. (1962). (*Synopses of the British Fauna*, No. 13). Linnean Society of London (address above). £1. plus postage.

The fullest modern work, lavishly illustrated.

"Census of the Distribution of British Non-marine Molluscs" (1951). *Journal of Conchology*, Vol. 23, Nos. 6 and 7, pages 172–243. 4*s*. (*See* "Societies", page 171.)

In this work the British Isles are divided into 148 "vice-counties" and the presence or absence of every species is noted for each, together with notes on ecology and habits and a distribution-map for each species.

CHAPTER 6. (Keeping Molluscs in captivity.)

"A Culture Method for Slugs", by J. W. Stephenson (1962). *Proceedings of the Malacological Society of London*, Vol. 25, Part 1, pages 43–45. £1. (*See* "Societies", page 171.)

CHAPTER 7. (Suggestions for observations and research)

"Slugs in Gardens; Their Numbers, Activities and Distribution", by H. F. Barnes and J. W. Weil (1944–5). *Journal of Animal Ecology*, Vol. 13, pages 140–175; Vol. 14, pages 71–105.
Apart from the direct information they contain, these two papers will give an idea of how to set about an ecological study.
"Area Effects in *Cepaea* on the Larkhill Artillery Ranges, Salisbury Plain", by A. J. Cain and D. J. Currey (1963). *Journal of the Linnean Society of London, Zoology*, Vol. 45, No. 303, pages 1–15.
This is the latest paper on the distribution and significance of banding-varieties in *Cepaea*, and contains references to others.
The World of Small Animals, by T. H. Savory (1955). University of London Press. 15s.
A valuable book, especially for younger readers, on the theme that any-one who takes up the study of a small and unfashionable group of animals can soon hope to become an expert in that group, and has a greater chance of making useful new observations than one who works on birds or butter-flies. A useful companion to the whole "Young Specialist" series.

For Still Further Reading

Most of the books and papers listed above contain references to others. All books and papers on molluscs published in the world are listed and cross-indexed in the "Mollusca" section of *The Zoological Record* (published annually by the Zoological Society of London, Regent's Park, London, N.W.1). Individual parts and back-numbers can be purchased for a few shillings, or complete runs of the publication studied in one of the larger libraries.

If you cannot buy or borrow any desired book or volume of a journal, your local public librarian will be pleased to obtain it for you from the National Central Library or the National Science Reference Library. The only charge to you will be the cost of return postage. The Science Library Photocopy Service, London, S.W.7 will locate and supply cheap photostat copies of any desired scientific paper.

Societies

Membership of the following specialist societies is open to those interested in molluscs. In each case the subscription covers copies of the society's journals for the year and the privilege of obtaining back-numbers at reduced prices.

The Conchological Society (annual subscription, £1; entrance fee, 10*s*.). Hon. Secretary Mr. T. E. Crowley, B.Sc., The Cottage, Church Street, Bampton, Oxon.

The Malacological Society (annual subscription £2; entrance fee, 10*s* 6*d*.). Hon. Secretary Dr. J. E. Rigby, Department of Biology, Queen Elizabeth College, Campden Hill Road, London, W.8.

Index to English and Latin Names

173

175

Some Common Synonyms

Many animals are lumbered with two or more scientific names. A full synonymy of the British non-marine Molluscs would make a substantial volume by itself. The following list has been prepared mainly so as to help readers to correlate this book with those by Ellis (1926) and Step (1945). (**Figures in bold type refer to the species numbers used in the text.**)

SYNONYM	NAME USED IN THIS BOOK
Acicula lineata (*non* Draparnaud)	*Acme fusca* (Montagu) **8**
Acmaea subcylindrica (L.)	*Truncatella subcylindrica* (L.) **16**
Agriolimax agrestis (*non* L.)	*Agriolimax reticulatus* (Müller) **102**
Alexia myosotis (Draparnaud)	*Phytia myosotis* (Draparnaud) **21**
Amnicola confusa (Frauenfeld)	*Pseudamnicola confusa* (Frauenfeld) **15**
taylori (Smith)	*Bythinella scholtzi* (Schmidt) **14**
Amphipeplea glutinosa (Müller)	*Myxas glutinosa* (Müller) **32**
Ancylastrum fluviatile (Müller)	*Ancylus fluviatilis* Müller **47**
Ancylus lacustris (L.)	*Acroloxus lacustris* (L.) **48**
Anodonta minima (Kennard, Salisbury & Woodward *non* Millet)	*Anodonta complanata* Rossmässler **159**
Aplecta hypnorum (L.)	*Aplexa hypnorum* (L.) **22**
Arion circumscriptus Johnston	*Arion fasciatus* (Nilsson) **94**
Ashfordia granulata (Alder)	*Monacha granulata* (Alder) **142**
Azeca tridens (Pulteney)	*Azeca goodalli* (Férussac) **55**
Bradybaena fruticum (Müller)	*Fruticicola fruticum* (Müller) **128**
Buliminus montanus (Draparnaud)	*Ena montana* (Draparnaud) **79**
Buliminus obscurus (Müller)	*Ena obscura* (Müller) **80**
Caecilianella acicula (Müller)	*Cecilioides acicula* (Müller) **87**
Caecilioides acicula (Müller)	*Cecilioides acicula* (Müller) **87**
Clausilia biplicata (Montagu)	*Laciniaria biplicata* (Montagu) **85**
laminata (Montagu)	*Marpessa laminata* (Montagu) **81**
rugosa (*non* Draparnaud)	*Clausilia bidentata* (Ström) **83**
Conulus fulvus (Müller)	*Euconulus fulvus* (Müller) **122**
Cyclostoma elegans (Müller)	*Pomatias elegans* (Müller) **7**
Deroceras spp.	*Agriolimax* spp. **102–105**

SYNONYM	NAME USED IN THIS BOOK
Eulota fruticum (Müller)	*Fruticicola fruticum* (Müller) **128**
Euparypha pisana (Müller)	*Theba pisana* (Müller) **132**
Ferussacia lubrica (Müller)	*Cochlicopa lubrica* (Müller) **56**
tridens (Pulteney)	*Azeca goodalli* (Férussac) **55**
Goniodiscus rotundatus (Müller)	*Discus rotundatus* (Müller) **124**
Helicella heripensis (Mabille)	*Helicella gigaxi* (L. Pfeiffer) **144**
Helix aculeata Müller	*Acanthinula aculeata* (Müller) **77**
acuta Müller	*Cochlicella acuta* (Müller) **149**
arbustorum L.	*Arianta arbustorum* (L.) **131**
cantiana Montagu	*Monacha cantiana* (Montagu) **141**
caperata Montagu	*Helicella caperata* (Montagu) **143**
cartusiana Müller	*Monacha cartusiana* (Müller) **140**
ericetorum Müller	*Helicella itala* (L.) **147**
fusca Montagu	*Hygromia subrufescens* (Miller) **135**
granulata Alder	*Monacha granulata* (Alder) **142**
heripensis (Mabille)	*Helicella gigaxi* (L. Pfeiffer) **144**
hispida L.	*Hygromia hispida* (L.) **138**
hortensis Müller	*Cepaea hortensis* (Müller) **151**
lamellata Jeffreys	*Acanthinula lamellata* (Jeffreys) **78**
lapicida L.	*Helicigona lapicida* (L.) **130**
nemoralis L.	*Cepaea nemoralis* (L.) **150**
obvoluta Müller	*Helicodonta obvoluta* (Müller) **129**
pisana Müller	*Theba pisana* (Müller) **132**
pulchella Müller	*Vallonia pulchella* (Müller) **75**
pygmaea Draparnaud	*Punctum pygmaeum* (Draparnaud) **123**
revelata Gray	*Hygromia subvirescens* (Bellamy) **139**
rotundata Müller	*Discus rotundatus* (Müller) **124**
rufescens (Da Costa)	*Hygromia striolata* (C. Pfeiffer) **136**
rupestris Draparnaud	*Pyramidula rupestris* (Draparnaud) **54**
virgata Da Costa	*Helicella virgata* (Da Costa) **145**
Hyalinia alliaria (Müller)	*Oxychilus alliarius* (Miller) **118**
cellaria (Müller)	*cellarius* (Müller) **117**
crystallina (Müller)	*Vitrea crystallina* (Müller) **111**
excavata (Alder)	*Zonitoides excavatus* (Alder) **121**
nitidula (Draparnaud)	*Retinella nitidula* (Draparnaud) **115**
nitidus (Müller)	*Zonitoides nitidus* (Müller) **120**
pura (Alder)	*Retinella pura* (Alder) **114**
radiatula (Alder)	*radiatula* (Alder) **113**
Hydrobia jenkinsi E. A. Smith	*Potamopyrgus jenkinsi* (E. A. Smith) **13**
similis Jeffreys	*Pseudamnicola confusa* (Frauenfeld) **15**

178

SYNONYM	NAME USED IN THIS BOOK
Lehmannia arborum (Bouchard-Chantereaux)	*Lehmannia marginata* (Müller) **106**
Leuconia bidentata (Montagu)	*Leucophytia bidentata* (Montagu) **20**
Limax agrestis L.	*Agriolimax agrestis* (L.) **103**
arborum Bouchard-Chantereaux	*Lehmannia marginata* (Müller) **106**
carinatus Risso .	*Milax sowerbyi* (Férussac) **109**
gagates Draparnaud	*gagates* (Draparnaud) **107**
laevis Müller	*Agriolimax laevis* (Müller) **104**
marginatus Müller	*Lehmannia marginata* (Müller) **106**
Limnaea spp.	*Lymnaea* spp. **24–31**
Lymnaea glutinosa (Müller)	*Myxas glutinosa* (Müller) **32**
pereger (Müller)	*Lymnaea peregra* (Müller) **28–29**
Milax gracilis (Leydig)	*Milax budapestensis* (Hazay) **110**
Neretina fluviatilis (L.)	*Theodoxus fluviatilis* (L.) **1**
Nerita elegans Müller	*Pomatias elegans* (Müller) **7**
fluviatilis L.	*Theodoxus fluviatilis* (L.) **1**
Oxychilus lucidus (Draparnaud)	*Oxychilus draparnaldi* (Beck) **116**
Peringia ulvae (Pennant)	*Hydrobia ulvae* (Pennant) **11**
Physa hypnorum (L.)	*Aplexa hypnorum* (L.) **22**
Pisidium cinereum Alder	*Pisidium casertanum* (Poli) **165**
conventrum (misprint)	*conventus* Clessin **166**
fontinale (Draparnaud)	*casertanum* (Poli) **165**
obtusalastrum Woodward .	*obtusale* (Lamarck) **173**
steenbuchii (Müller)	*casertanum* (Poli) **165**
Planorbis complanatus Jeffreys (*non* L.)	*Planorbis planorbis* (L.) **35**
complanatus (L.)	*Segmentina complanata* (L.) **46**
corneus (L.)	*Planorbarius corneus* (L.) **33**
dilatatus Gould	*Menetus dilatatus* (Gould) **34**
glaber Forbes & Hanley	*Planorbis laevis* Alder **42**
nautileus (L.)	*crista* (L.) **44**
spirorbis (L.) (*nom. dub.*)	*leucostoma* Millet **38**
umbilicatus Müller	*planorbis* (L.) **35**
Pupa alpestris (Alder)	*Vertigo alpestris* Alder **64**
angustior (Jeffreys)	*angustior* Jeffreys **61**
antivertigo Draparnaud	*antivertigo* (Draparnaud) **67**
edentula Draparnaud	*Columella edentula* (Draparnaud) **58**
lilljeborgi (Westerlund)	*Vertigo lilljeborgi* Westerlund **69**
minutissima Hartmann	*Truncatellina cylindrica* (Férussac) **59**
moulinsiana Dupuy	*Vertigo moulinsiana* (Dupuy) **68**
pusilla (Müller)	*pusilla* Müller **62**
pygmaea Draparnaud	*pygmaea* (Draparnaud) **63**

179

SYNONYM	NAME USED IN THIS BOOK
Pupa secale Draparnaud	*Abida secale* (Draparnaud) **70**
substriata (Jeffreys)	*Vertigo substriata* Jeffreys **66**
Pupilla anglica (Wood)	*Lauria anglica* (Wood) **73**
cylindracea (Da Costa)	*cylindracea* (Da Costa) **72**
Sabanaea ulvae (Pennant)	*Hydrobia ulvae* (Pennant) **11**
Sabinea ulvae (Pennant)	*ulvae* (Pennant) **11**
Sphaerium pallidum (Gray)	*Sphaerium transversum* (Say) **163**
Succinea elegans Jeffreys *non* Risso	*Succinea pfeifferi* Rossmässler **50**
Theba cantiana (Montagu)	*Monacha cantiana* (Montagu) **141**
cartusiana (Montagu)	*cartusiana* (Montagu) **140**
Trichia hispida (L.)	*Hygromia hispida* (L.) **138**
striolata (C. Pfeiffer)	*striolata* (C. Pfeiffer) **136**
subvirescens (Bellamy)	*subvirescens* (Bellamy) **139**
Trochoidea elegans (Gmelin)	*Helicella elegans* (Gmelin) **148**
Unio margaritifera (L.)	*Margaritifera margaritifera* (L.) **154**
Viviparus contectus Miller	*Viviparus fasciatus* (Müller) **3**